UNDERGROUND RAILWAYS OF THE WORLD

Underground
Railways
of the World

Their History and Development

H. C. P. HAVERS

B.A.(Cantab.), A.M.I.C.E., A.M.I.Mech.E.

TEMPLE PRESS BOOKS   LONDON 1966

First published 1966 for
TEMPLE PRESS BOOKS
by
GEORGE NEWNES LTD.
Tower House, Southampton Street, London, WC2

© 1966, HAROLD CHARLES PERCIVAL HAVERS

Printed in Great Britain by
Cox & Wyman Limited, London, Fakenham and Reading

Contents

v

KEY TO MAPS (EXCEPT CENTRAL LONDON)

Underground in service
Open to the air in service
Underground being constructed
Open to the air being constructed
Planned for the near future

List of Plates

viii

Preface

This book is about underground railways, and the history and development of railways which have been built underground as a deliberate policy in densely populated areas. Most of them come up for air as they run out into the dormitory suburbs and many of them then become 'elevated', but the book cannot afford space to deal in much detail with the open-air sections or with the many urban railways which go below ground only for short distances as a matter of convenience.

It has also been necessary to distinguish between railways and tramways on which cars are coupled together to make trains and often run over their own rights of way and in tunnels. The distinction adopted is between railway trains controlled by a system of signalling and trains, or street cars, which are driven by sight.

Future developments present another problem. New lines and extensions are planned but, before construction starts, policies and traffic requirements change and the final works are often very different from those planned. Only those proposals which appear to be certain to be implemented in the next few years are briefly described.

In quoting figures regarding systems which use the metric measurements it is thought convenient to give, in parenthesis, the approximate equivalent in the English system, and it should be understood that the metric figures are accurate and the others are rounded.

Finally it is a pleasure to acknowledge, with gratitude, the willing help given by many organizations in providing the data and photographs and giving permission to use them. Generous assistance has been given by the following underground railway authorities and companies:

BARCELONA *Ferrocarril de Sarria da Barcelona S.A. & Ferrocarril Metropolitano de Barcelona S.A.*

BERLIN *Berliner Verkehrs-Betriebe (B.V.G.)*

BOSTON *Massachusetts Bay Transportation Authority*

BUDAPEST *Hungarian News and Information Service*

BUENOS AIRES *Subterranees de Buenos Aires*

KIEV *Kiev Metropolitan Railway*

CHICAGO *Chicago Transit Authority*

GLASGOW *Glasgow Corporation Transport*

HAMBURG *Hamburger Hochbahn A.G.*

LENINGRAD *Leningrad Metropolitan Railway*

LISBON *Metropolitano de Lisboa*

LONDON *London Transport*

MADRID *Metropolitano de Madrid*

MILAN *Azienda Transporti Municipali Milano*

MONTREAL *City of Montreal Public Works Department*

MOSCOW *Moscow Lenin Metropolitan*

NAGOYA *Nagoya City Transit Bureau*

NEW YORK *New York City Transit Authority*

OSAKA *Osaka Municipal Transportation Bureau*

OSLO *Oslo Kommune Tunnelbanekontoret*

PARIS *Regie Autonome des Transports Parisiens*

PHILADELPHIA *Philadelphia Transportation Company*

ROME *Societa per Azione Delle Tramvie e Ferrovie Elettriche di Roma*

ROTTERDAM *Rotterdamse Elektrische Tram*

STOCKHOLM *A.B. Stockholms Sparvagar*

TOKIO *Teito Rapid Transit Authority & Tokio Metropolitan Government*

TORONTO *Toronto Transit Commission*

VIENNA *Wiener Stadtwerke Verkehrsbetriebe*

PART I *General*

Early Years

The tracks of primitive man and his animals zigzagged up steep hills and wound about on the firmer ground of marshy valleys. In more level and dry countries he learnt to drag loads upon sledges, then to use logs as rollers beneath heavy loads, but the logs were left behind as the load moved on and much labour was involved in carrying them ahead for further use. The invention of the wheel, which moved forward with the load, was a decisive break-through. The first wheeled vehicle of which any record remains was used in Mesopotamia some time between 3000 and 4000 b.c. Although the early wheels were broad to carry heavy loads, they required harder and smoother surfaces and soft places were filled in with stones. As loads became heavier four wheels became necessary, and the tracks had to be made straighter until steering by a pivoted axle was invented. The straight, hard Roman military roads were the forerunners of the modern motorways, but the civil population continued to struggle on for centuries without any organization for the maintenance of their deeply rutted highways and local roads.

For many years wheels were guided by ruts which were patched and filled with stone to provide a hard surface. Then the idea of plate-laying was born. Stone slabs were laid and, later, iron plates with flanges to guide the wheels, but finally some genius thought of putting the flange on the wheel and running it along a raised surface. This was the first challenge in the war between road and rail.

In the 19th century the railways looked like winning with the advantages of greater speed, smoother travel and a more permanent way. The internal combustion engine and the pneumatic tyre changed this and brought into prominence the flexibility of road travel. For short journeys and small loads individual transport direct from point to point has become a modern necessity. Bulk transport is only advantageous when the freight or

3

passengers originate within one small area and are destined for another, but it is cheaper than individual transport for the same reasons that any mass-produced goods are cheaper than purpose-made items.

At last it is being realized that the railways must be used for bulk long-distance transport and, if individual and short distance transport is to be efficient, bulk traffic must be kept off the roads. It is a simple matter of economics on a national scale which has long been obscured by the fact that the railways attempt to cover their costs by a direct and open charge to the customer, while the cost of road travel is very largely paid by taxation. Property and land is acquired; roads are built; improved and maintained; traffic signs and signals are installed; police and traffic wardens control the motorist; all at no direct charge to the motorist or haulier, unless you count the occasional fine. When one realizes the economic truth it becomes a question of how much the individual is prepared to pay for the convenience of individual transport, in money or in time.

Over long distances the problem of traffic congestion has scarcely become apparent, as yet, but the race between the motor manufacturers and the road builders has started. There seems to be no limit to the number of vehicles that can be made, but there must be a limit to the proliferation of roads. Whole nations are heading towards strangulation by individual transport, a disease against which many great cities have struggled for centuries.

In London hackney carriages were introduced in 1625 and followed by four-wheeled 'growlers' in 1805. The Shillibeer horse omnibus came in 1829 and unmanœuvreable horse trams in 1861. The agile two-wheeled 'Hansom' cabs corresponded to the small cars of today and had the same knack of causing confusion by their extreme mobility. Road improvements and potentially faster vehicles have scarcely improved matters, and the speed of traffic in London's streets is practically the same as a century ago.

The cities of the world have proved that mass transport and individual transport cannot mix successfully in urban areas. Yet when railways offered a separate mass transport system the cities were reluctant to accept. Many municipalities insisted on railway stations being kept beyond their boundaries, and the great London termini are arranged in a ring around the central area. The first penetration by a railway was the world's first underground line, the Metropolitan, opened on January 10, 1863. In spite of the very unpleasant conditions created by the steam engine, it was an instant success.

In America a different method of 'grade-separation' was favoured. The first so-called 'monorail' was built for the World Fair at Philadelphia in 1876. This carried passengers for the Fair across a valley a quarter of a mile wide and up to 30ft deep, on a single loadbearing rail fixed on top of a triangular beam. A 60-seat coach had three compartments, one on top and one at either side below rail level, and was guided by solid rubber-tyred wheels on rails mounted on the lower corners of the triangular beam. The coal-fired locomotive was balanced by water tanks below rail level on both sides. This was not a great success but the promoter, General Stone, persisted and more conventional types of elevated railway were installed in many of the great cities of America. London, however, preferred to go underground and built herself an extensive network of steam lines extending through the rapidly expanding suburbs into new dormitory areas in the surrounding country.

The next step forward in the development of urban transport came with the application of electric traction. Werner von Siemens demonstrated an electric railway at Berlin in 1879, Magnus Volk opened an electric line along the English sea-shore at Brighton in 1883, and in Ireland the Bessbrook and Newry railway was electrically operated in 1885.

The development of electric traction coincided so closely with the building of the first deep tube railway that the City and South London tube opened in 1890 with electric power, although when construction started in 1886 it was intended to be worked by cable and steam winch. The electrification of existing underground railways followed rapidly and, on the surface, the electric tram gained great favour. The first electric tramway was the Franz Joseph Line in Pest, opened in 1897; and on the inauspicious date of Friday, May 13, 1898, a short line opened at the Alexandra Palace in London, operating for 600 yards over an average gradient of 1 in 13. The international interest in electric traction was emphasized by this line, which was built by a German

5

company who were agents for two American manufacturers, and had an Austrian chief engineer trained in France.

Though tramways in streets are now a major cause of traffic congestion, and most great cities intend to remove them as soon as possible, they have been the proving ground for many developments adopted by underground railways. The Glasgow system was electrified by installing an existing pattern of tram motor in the railway cars, and the modern underground railway motor owes much to developments made in tramcars. Welded rails were first used by tramways many years before London Transport introduced their full-scale use for a railway in 1939. The rubber-sprung wheels of the new Milan underground and the latest vehicles on the Hamburg Hochbahn are similar to those used on tramcars early in this century. In Vienna the tramways are going underground, trains of tramcars are coupled up, and the result is an embryo underground railway system.

For a short time the trolleybus appeared as the tramways logical successor, with the advantage of manœuvrability and the smooth silent running of pneumatic tyres. The cost of operation is about the same as the somewhat noisier and much slower motor bus, but the facts that the trolley must follow a fixed route, irrespective of traffic diversions or road repairs, and that a power failure can bring the whole system to a halt with the streets obstructed by unmovable vehicles, has led to a preference for the bus. The bus has an essential role to play in any city's transport system as a feeder to the underground routes and for services where the traffic is too sparse for a railway to work economically. It is not a suitable vehicle for heavy commuter traffic over any appreciable distance, and to solve the street traffic problem the commuter must be taken off the streets.

A sub-surface railway is one that is near the surface and can be reached from the street very quickly. It is obviously more convenient than a deeper tube line which must be served by lifts or escalators, but it cannot always be built. In a hilly area railways cannot follow the contour of the ground as the maximum gradient is usually considered to be about 1 in 25 for short distances and 1 in 60 for longer grades. It may also be that the nature of the subsoil makes it difficult to construct shallow tunnels or that the line must go to a considerable depth to pass under deep rivers or

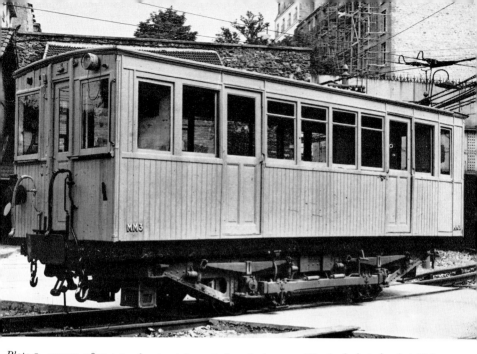

Plate 1 PARIS *1899 type of motor, taken out of service in 1904. Wooden body 7·6 m (25 ft) long on a steel frame with two axles.*

Plate 2 PARIS *A pneumatic tyred train which entered service in 1963 (1959 type).*

Plate 3 LONDON *A locomotive and car of the City & South London Line as delivered in 1900. The end platform has lattice gates io be operated by the guard and it was considered unnecessary to provide windows when there was no view.*

Plate 4 NEW YORK *A new Flushing Line train of the 'Brightliner' stock which worked to the Worlds' Fair. The exterior finish is blue paint and stainless steel heavily corrugated.*

inlets of the sea. It is a curious fact that the Press, and consequently the public, seem to be unable to grasp the essential and obvious differences between tube and sub-surface lines in London, but persist in referring to the whole of the underground system as 'the tube'.

London can claim priority both in the construction of underground railways and in tunnelling under a river. The first attempt to drive a road tunnel under the Thames was between Rotherhithe and Limehouse. A small pilot tunnel had been driven 1000 ft. out of the proposed 1,200 ft. when, on January 26, 1808, the water broke through and caused the abandonment of the scheme.

The invention of the tunnel shield by Marc Brunel in 1818 led to a second attempt and, after considerable financial and engineering difficulties, including flood, a vehicular tunnel was opened between Rotherhithe and Wapping on March 25, 1843. This became the first under river railway tunnel in 1869 when the London, Brighton and South Coast Railway used it for a service of 23 trains a day from their main lines at New Cross. The resident engineer who completed the tunnel was the son of Marc Brunel, the famous Isambard Kingdom Brunel.

The Brunel shield was of cast iron, divided into 36 compartments in each of which one man worked excavating to a depth of 4½ in. The shield was then jacked forward from the brickwork already in place to enable another ring of 4½-in bricks to be inserted. This system was developed into a circular shield by Barlow, who conceived the idea while sinking iron cylinders for a bridge about 1862, and in 1867 published the idea of a network of deep-level tubes.

The world's first tube railway was opened on August 2, 1870, under the Thames from Tower Hill to Vine Street, a distance of a quarter of a mile. This had a cast iron segmental lining, grouted in after completion and, though the internal diameter was only 6 ft 7 in, it was remarkably similar in construction to all the later London tubes. The tunnel reached a depth of 66 ft below high water level, was reached by 50-ft deep shafts 10 ft in diameter with steam-worked lifts, and the passengers travelled in a single car hauled upon a 2-ft 6-in gauge track by a cable, winch and steam engine.

With tickets costing a penny (or twopence if one was in a hurry

B

to pass ahead of other passengers) and, with only 12 seats in the car, the project could not pay its way and the railway was removed. Spiral staircases were put in the shafts and the tunnel became a pedestrian subway, charging a halfpenny toll, until Tower Bridge was opened in 1894. At the present time it is used as a pipe subway.

Greathead perfected the circular shield which still bears his name, and he was the engineer of the first successful tube railway, the City and South London, now part of the Northern Line.

The latest development in this type of shield is a rotating digger drum within the shield which cuts into the soil, and breaks it into pieces for removal by conveyor belt. This has had considerable use on the tunnels of hydraulic schemes, and can be driven very fast at the expense of some difficulty of control. The problem of keeping the shield on line and level with sufficient accuracy for railway tunnels has not yet been fully solved.

The men who built the first London tubes had the shield but not the machinery to make a large circular tunnel and line it with heavy cast iron plates in one operation. The station tunnels were built by enlarging a smaller one, but to have used this method for long tunnels would have been extremely expensive and therefore the size of the running tunnels was small, by modern standards. When the tubes have been extended there has been no advantage in using larger tunnels for rolling stock which must be small enough to pass through the older parts of the system; however, a slight enlargement from 11 ft 8¼ in to 12 ft 0 in diameter has frequently been made to provide better clearances, and many sections of old tunnel have been enlarged, for the same reason, where the alignment was not very accurate.

A tube tunnel is an expensive structure. Any addition to the diameter causes more than a threefold addition to the lining material, and the quantity of soil to be excavated and removed increases in proportion to the square of the diameter. To make the rolling stock as large as possible the clearances are made as small as is safe. Therefore the tubes must be accurately built and the track must be rigidly located in them, therefore it is almost invariably set in concrete. With the development of mechanical means of excavation and removal of spoil, there has been a great saving of expensive labour. The extra cost of the larger tubes now being built is greatly reduced by the more economical means of excavation, and disposal of the spoil, which can be installed in the larger tunnel. The increased size of the rolling stock gives a greater line capacity and effects economies in building and maintaining rolling stock of a more standard type.

Later Developments

The first sub-surface tunnels were built by 'cut and cover'. This very descriptive term implies cutting a trench, building a tunnel in it and then covering it over again. The old tunnels roofed with arches skilfully formed with several layers of brick, took a long time to build, but bricks have the advantage that no shuttering is required. In Berlin and Hamburg very elaborately waterproofed tunnels were necessary and a thin brick wall carrying the water-proofing sheeting was used as shuttering, that is to support the vertical face of the concrete walls until it had hardened. Tunnels are now generally made of concrete cast *in situ* and reinforced with steel rods, but the use of precast sections is increasing and Hamburg has used short sections of complete tunnel six or seven feet long to build up long continuous lengths. The most recent, and very ingenious, developments are described in the chapters on Tokyo and Rotterdam.

The alternative to cut and cover is the 'Belgian' system of mining without disturbing the surface. Small galleries are driven from a pit and these are then enlarged to the full tunnel section. These pilot headings are easy to support against caving in, and give warning of any difficult ground before it is reached by the major excavation. The chief anxiety is caused by the tendency of the roof to fall in and it is not unusual to excavate the upper portion of the tunnel first and to complete the roof before cutting away the ground below (as in Chicago), or even to use a semi-circular shield for the roof portion (as in Tokyo). The most recent and interesting development was first used in Milan and has been adopted in several other countries to reduce noise and vibration or damage to foundations in places where this was more important than expense.

To solve the street traffic problem it is necessary not only to provide a comprehensive underground railway system, but also to persuade passengers to use it. The regular user of public transport will travel by the system with the lowest fare if it is reasonably quick and comfortable.

The cost of operation is therefore a very important field for development work. Taking the London Transport system as an example, the average charge per mile, in 1962, was 2·61 pence on central buses and 2·35 pence on the underground railways. The working expenses were about £7000 a year for a bus and £6600 for an underground railway car, but only 4½ weekly paid men are required for each bus, compared with 7 for each railway car. This is in spite of the fact that a bus, carrying an average load of 16½ passengers throughout the day, and an 8-car train, averaging only 15 passengers, both require the same crew of two. On the whole London Transport system staff costs represent nearly 75 per cent of the operating expenditure, and a reduction of staff could contribute greatly to lowering fares and attracting more passengers.

All over the world tickets are being sold from automatic machines rather than by human beings. In most cities there is a fixed fare for any distance or for travel within a specified area, and it is sufficient to check that every passenger has a ticket. To attract customers the fare must be low and consequently the long-distance traveller does not pay his share, but it is not easy to change such a system once it is established. In forming the elaborate proposals for an urban railway in San Francisco a detailed study is being made of systems for automatic checking and collecting of a great variety of tickets, and in London a pilot scheme is in operation with a view to general adoption within the next few years.

Station staff can also be reduced by the use of closed circuit television to enable one man to keep an eye upon two or more platforms, concourses or station entrances. This development is being followed up on many systems, notably the new Milan Metro.

Signal operating staff is being reduced by automatic signalling. The old signal cabin was operated by long levers necessary to overcome the friction and weight of mechanical interlocking and, in very early days, the rodding or cables which connected them to the points and signals. The first step was to operate points and signals electrically or by electrically controlled pneumatic machinery—remote control of the track apparatus. This was soon followed by electrical interlocking apparatus which enabled all movements to be effected by miniature levers or push buttons operated very quickly and easily and enabling one man to work a large and busy complex of lines.

With the development of electrical interlocking it became possible to set up a complete route by pressing a single button which set the signals and points correctly for a train to pass through a junction, and which prevented any conflicting movement being made. It is now possible for the signalman to set up a route for one train and, before it has passed, to operate the appropriate button for the correct routing of the next train. The second route is automatically set up after the first train has passed clear of the junction.

A logical development was to arrange for one central signal box to control and operate the apparatus of one or more other cabins in the same way that the electrical substations are remotely controlled, enabling staff to be withdrawn from them. The individual cabins are still fully equipped for independent operation in the event of a breakdown of the control or any other emergency.

The extent to which automatic signalling is a profitable investment clearly depends upon the number of junctions on the system, their complexity, and the frequency of the train service. On a complicated, heavily worked line, full automation of the signalling can be attained. The whole of the central area of London's underground is automatically operated and much of the New York system, which is steadily becoming more complicated with many new connections between the individual lines. The operation of a whole day's service is indicated on a roll by punched holes, and the 'programme machine' interprets this and arranges for every train to make a complete journey over the right route, at the right time, in complete safety. It is only necessary for the central control staff to watch the working of the trains and take action on the few occasions when something unusual happens.

On most systems it has always been the practice to have two staff on every train. Milan and Hamburg are exceptions. They use television to enable the station staff to perform the guard's duty of ensuring the safety of passengers at the station, and both are moving towards automatic driving of trains.

The many experiments in automatic signalling and driving are designed not so much to reduce staff, or to reduce the responsibility of the driver, as to secure a mechanical regularity in the service and increased safety. Acceleration and braking are extremely expensive and if every train can be made to use them to the best advantage there is a great saving of traction current, brake and rail wear and rolling stock maintenance, as well as a smoother, more comfortable ride for the passengers, and a more regular service unaffected by the vagaries of individual drivers.

Automatic driving is not expected to give any considerable increase in speed or in line capacity. The maximum attainable speed over any line depends upon the distance between stations, and upon the rate of acceleration and braking, which are normally limited to about 3 m.p.h. per second by the comfort of passengers, particularly standing passengers. The actual overall speed attained depends upon the lengths of station stops, which are largely determined by the behaviour of the passengers and their efficient control by the station staff. In this the use of television is a great help.

The line capacity is expressed in the number of passengers that can be carried in an hour and this depends upon a number of factors. To understand this it is helpful to think first about the 'line capacity' of an escalator. If it is running more quickly it obviously will carry more passengers to the surface in any given time than a slower escalator. But there comes a time, as the speed is increased, when passengers do not step on close together and only alternate steps are occupied as the escalator moves up. At this speed, about 150 ft per minute, the capacity of the escalator falls suddenly. Each passenger reaches the top more quickly but if there is a crowd waiting to go up, most of them will be delayed. In the same way, if passengers are allowed to walk up an escalator they space themselves out farther apart and, though individual passengers make a quicker journey, the capacity of the escalator is reduced and it is carrying up fewer persons per minute or per hour.

In the same manner, if the speed of trains is increased they must, for safety, travel farther apart. One may have fewer faster trains, or more trains travelling more slowly, but there is one particular speed and number of trains which will give the maximum line capacity. One way to increase the capacity is to ensure that the trains can travel close to each other, particularly when approaching a station. This is done by speed control signalling, a system by which a signal will not clear unless the speed of an approaching train has been reduced sufficiently to ensure safety. The most usual application is upon home signals, to allow a train to approach more closely behind one stopped in a station.

Another step towards increased line capacity is the use of longer trains. On the older systems the platforms were built for comparatively short trains and on practically all of them lengthening of the platforms has been going on for some years.

Underground railways have their greatest value in moving the heavy commuter traffic, and line capacity must be provided on the basis of the peak hour travel. In New York, 10-car trains run at 32 per hour and, each carrying 3000 passengers, can move 96,000 passengers per hour, which would require a bus every two seconds or 16 private cars per second, at the average loading. In the slack periods the rolling stock, expensive signalling and other installations are being little used, but must be paid for. Little can be done about this except to attract passengers who, at that time, are generally in no great hurry and find surface transport in the less crowded streets reasonably quick and very convenient.

The underground railways are always engaged in direct competition with bus services and private cars, and the extent to which underground traffic can fluctuate is not generally realized. The Paris Metro is a good example with its intricate network, close stations, and easy access from the street. In 1946 the traffic reached a peak, of nearly 1600 million journeys, at a time when bus services and private cars were few. By 1953 it had fallen by 37 per cent to little over 1000 million, but has now recovered to about 1200 million—only 75 per cent of the 1946 figure.

Comfort and speed in the trains are necessary to attract custom. New cars are obviously more comfortable and pleasant to ride in, with better seating and lighting, with a more cheerful style of decoration and, in some instances, sound-absorbing linings. But these are minor improvements in comparison with the bold advance made by Paris with its pneumatic tyred vehicles, a lead now followed by Montreal. Other systems are reluctant to introduce this entirely different type of bogie, which would call for separate maintenance depots, apparatus, and staff for maintenance, would mean keeping a second expensive stock of spare parts, and would prevent the free interchange of trains with the existing or unconverted lines. Another objection often raised about systems where the lines come into the open is that there is some danger of snow becoming packed under the wheels and raising the guiding wheels out of engagement with the guide rails.

The success of the Paris experiment has also led to a revival of interest in a system of guiding railway vehicles patented in 1931. This employs guiding wheels set at an angle of about 45 degrees and running on either side of a single central guide rail. A turnout could be quite simply formed by two diverging guide rails joined to the straight portion by a single movable switch tongue. There need be no crossing of the guide rails and, because they would be always at a lower level than the tracks on which the rubber tyres would run, they would cross them in simple diagonal grooves. The simplicity of this invention for junction work is clear, but the Parisian use of the conductor rails for guidance is also economical, and the single guide rail provides no 'safety' wheels or rails in case of the (admittedly unlikely) deflation of a number of pneumatic tyres. However, it is a possible system for the equipment of a new line.

Following the use of pneumatic tyres on trains, there have been many proposals for overhead lines on the tri-rail system, with cars suspended from one rail and guided by two others, and using pneumatic tyres. The system claims all the advantages apparent in the Paris Metro installation, and no doubt it would obviate the nuisance of noise which some designs of considerable aesthetic merit have produced. It is not easy to visualize such a system in a city of narrow streets, and where the roads are straight and wide, trains running beneath them have obvious advantages. An overhead system may well provide a fast service in open country, but cannot be considered as a competitor to underground railways in the great cities.

We have seen that with stations close together the speed of travel can only be improved by better behaviour of the passengers, but where lines stretch into the country to stations far apart, a high maximum speed is valuable. It can be expected to attract customers where the trains run alongside or in the centre strip of a highway, an increasingly common sight in America, and motorists can actually see the train outstripping them in the race to the city.

But high speed and the sustained acceleration necessary to reach it are expensive in traction current. This expense can be reduced by making the trains lighter and consequently we have cars with aluminium alloy bodies, or stainless steel cars which need no separate underframe, dispensing with a heavy 'chassis' as modern automobile designers have done. Improved control gear also prevents the natural tendency for acceleration to fall off as the speed increases, or to vary with the weight of passengers carried. Generally these developments are aimed at reducing cost and any gain in speed is incidental.

New stations are commonly built with spacious, well lighted and decorated concourses which give an impression of freedom to move, and often an opportunity to gaze at shop windows. Tickets are sold or collected in sub-surface concourses which have many well planned entrances from the pavements or direct from large shops of office blocks, and underground stations are being integrated with the other amenities of a city. A striking example is the new Hibiya station in Tokyo, where the station structure includes a 60-ft motorway below the main street, a wide concourse and pedestrian passage at a lower level and finally the track and platforms about 50 ft below street level.

Such elaborate provisions for the comfort and convenience of passengers and strenuous efforts to attract them below are comparatively easy in the course of new construction, but to make a just appraisal of the world's underground railways it is essential to emphasize the difficulties of the older systems in altering their existing facilities to approach the same high standards of amenity. To remodel a station without inconvenience to passengers, loss of goodwill and a consequent diminution of traffic, is both difficult and extremely expensive. The cost of the many new track connections planned on the New York system, and of the Victoria Line in London, with all the rebuilding of interchange stations and diversion of existing tubes, must be at least double that of equivalent new construction.

The older generation face great difficulties in keeping up with progress, but the reader would certainly be surprised by a knowledge of the extent to which visits are made and common problems are discussed by those responsible for operating and constructing urban railways in all parts of the world.

All the recent developments of underground railway transport are receiving very detailed study by the Bay Area authorities of San Francisco, who have in mind the construction of a rapid transport system of 120 route miles which may be underground for some 24 miles, and pass under San Francisco Bay. When the final details are settled one may expect the system to present a complete summing up of world underground railway development to date.

PART II *Underground Railways of the World*

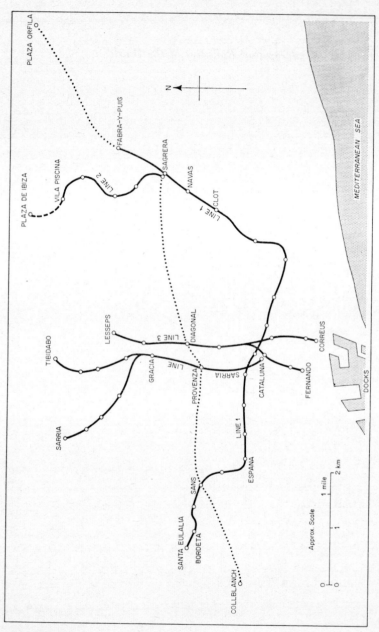

BARCELONA

Barcelona

Barcelona is the Manchester of Spain, famous for cotton and a variety of manufactures, and exporting wine, olives and cork. The harbour from which the Phoenicians sailed is picturesque in an area of narrow streets and ancient buildings, but the modern city, in which the bulk of the 1½ million inhabitants live and work, is one of wide boulevards running north and south to form a chequer board of fine buildings.

The underground system is being developed very rapidly, but at present it consists only of three lines, 1, 2 and 3, operated by the municipal Ferrocarril Metropolitano which took them over in June 1961, and the Sarria Line operated by a private company.

The most important is Line 1, the Transversal, which carries 130 million passengers a year across the city from east to west over a distance of 10·1 km (6⅓ miles)—with 18 stations—of which 8·9 km (5½ miles) are in tunnel.

Line 2, a short line of 2·68 km (1⅝ miles) and 5 stations between Vilapiscina and Sagrera in the north-east, is of particular interest as it is being used for service trials of automatic operation with a view to introducing this for all trains on Line 1. This line and the Woodford–Hainault section of London Transport are the only lines in service where intermediate stations are served by automatic trains.

The Gran Metropolitano, Line 3, runs southwards from Lesseps to Aragon in the centre of the city, and then in two branches to Fernando and Correos in the harbour district, having a total length of 5·2 km (3¼ miles) and 10 stations.

The Sarria Line runs parallel with Line 3 from Cataluna in the city centre and turns off westwards to connect with the surface railway at Sarria, a branch from Gracia to Tibidabo in the north giving it a total length of 6½ km (4 miles) and 12 stations.

Line 1 was designed to form a double track connection across the city for the National Railway and has adopted their track gauge of 1·672 m (5 ft 6 in) and is in a rectangular tunnel 8 m (26 ft 3 in) wide and 5·5 m (18 ft) high from rail level. The tracks are ballasted with timber sleepers and 50 kg/m (101 lb/yd) flat-bottomed rails in 18 m (59 ft) lengths. There is a central conductor rail of 37 kg/m (74·5 lb/yd) weight, carrying 1500 V d.c. fed from sub-stations near the tunnel portals at Bordeta and near Sagrera.

Traffic is carried in trains of two motors, with a trailer attached to the newer stock. Twelve motor cars constructed in 1926 are still running and are remarkable for their length of 21·7 m (71 ft 2 in), weight of 54·8 tons, and capacity of 54 seats and, in a crush, nearly 400 standing passengers, served by only three doorways on each side. The fleet of 46 motors includes 30 of modern design, and there are 20 similar trailers with a length of $16\frac{1}{2}$ m (54 ft 2 in) with longitudinal seating for 33 and a maximum crush capacity of 350. Ten of these motors weigh $39\frac{1}{3}$ tons and twenty $41\frac{1}{3}$ tons, while half the trailers weigh just under and half just over 28 tons. All have four double doors on each side. To allow for further increase in the 130 million passengers a year on Line 1, an order has been placed for another 40 motor cars and 10 trailers.

The stations of Line 1 vary considerably in design with side platforms 4 m (16 ft 5 in) wide or, at the terminals of Santa Eulalia and Fabra-y-Puig, an island platform of 4 or 5 m (13 ft or 16 ft 5 in) and two side platforms $3\frac{1}{2}$ m (11 ft 6 in) wide. Cataluna is the most important station and here the Line 1 station is built upon an underground bridge over the tracks of Line 3. Passages provide interchange also with the Sarria Line and the National Railway system.

The first section, Bordeta to Cataluna, was opened in June 1926, was extended at both ends to Triunfino and Santa Eulalia in July 1932, and on to Marinas in April 1933. Further development was held up by the civil disturbances until June 1951 when the line was taken on to Clot, to Navas in May 1953, and finally to Fabra-y-Puig in May 1954.

Line 2 is the most recent, having opened on July 21, 1959, and was used by over 13 million people in 1963. The line is wholly underground but operates upon an overhead system of 1260 V d.c. with a track gauge of 1·435 m (4 ft $8\frac{1}{2}$ in). The 14 motor cars, delivered in 1959, are $16\frac{1}{2}$ m (54 ft 2 in) long, weigh $36\frac{1}{2}$ tons, seat

Plate 5 LONDON *Kings Cross station platform in 1863. The double gauge of the track on the original Metropolitan Line is clearly shown by the artist.*

Plate 6 MOSCOW *Kropotkin station with a wide 'avenue' effect given by the pillars and vaulted ceiling the concourse between the platforms.*

Plate 7 LONDON *A typical programme machine. Such a machine operates the trains in one directic through a complicated junction of this area throughout the day without human intervention.*

Plate 8 MILAN *The station entrance is controlled by television. The two screens give a view of t platforms. On the right of them is a large switch to connect one or other screen, a switch for long or sho focus on the camera, and the adjustments for the set. Beyond, on the extreme right, are the switches f holding a train or allowing it to depart.*

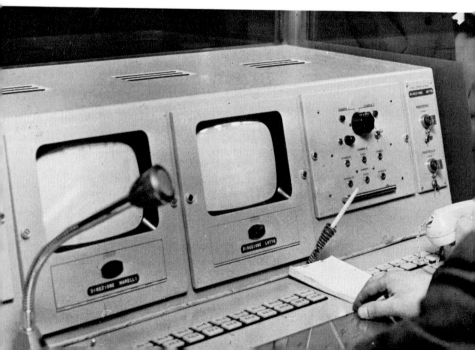

33 passengers with a crush load of 300 and have four doors each side.

Line 3 is also wholly underground with 1·435 m (4 ft 8½ in) gauge and an overhead system of 1300 V d.c. The 20 motor cars and 20 trailers vary in age but are all 14·3 m (46 ft 11 in) long, seating 12 passengers and capable of carrying 260 as a maximum. The line was opened on the last day of 1924 and is on a small scale with platforms from 77 m (263 ft) to 50 m (164 ft) long and 3 m (9 ft 10 in) maximum width. The traffic amounts to 57 million passengers a year, and an additional 18 motor cars have been ordered.

The independent Sarria Line was originally part of the Cataluna steam-operated, surface railway, but the urban section was rebuilt in tunnel and opened in 1954. Like Line 3, it has standard gauge and an overhead system of 1300 V d.c. The rolling stock consists only of eight very modern streamlined motor cars with four double doors on each side which work in pairs over the main line to Sarria and singly to Tibidabo.

On all the four lines, the basic signalling is by automatic block but, after experiments with a system of automatic driving which employed sliding contacts to pass signals to the train, an entirely new system was used upon one train which started trial running on June 1, 1963, over Line 2.

The automatic control is achieved by a means very different from that being experimented with on so many underground systems, and relies upon light sensitive cells to operate relays in the control system of the motor. The motor car carries a light fixed between two light-sensitive cells under the car. The relays are normally excited by the light illuminating the cells. When required, this light is cut off by screens placed upon the track, parallel to, but between, the rails and supported by brackets from the sleepers (Plate 11).

To explain the working of the apparatus we may follow the sequence of operations between two stations.

The train is at rest with the doors open. The doors are closed by the driver and the closing of the doors applies power so that the train accelerates. A screen on the right-hand side is then encountered and this cuts off current, allowing the train to coast. After some distance it is necessary to brake slightly, perhaps

c

because of a down gradient, and a screen to the left of the centre initiates a slow progressive application of the brakes. In a short while speed has been reduced as required, and a second right-hand screen locks the brake controller so that the degree of braking is constant and the train coasts at a steady speed. A station is now approached and a second left-hand screen causes a full service brake application. Finally, as the speed falls, the air brake is operated to bring the train to a halt.

Control by signals is obtained by placing both a right-hand and a left-hand screen. When the signal is clear both these screens are illuminated by lights upon the track. Consequently the reflection from the screens prevents the cells from being de-energized by the interruption to the light carried on the motor car, and the screens have no controlling effect. On the other hand, if the signal is at danger the lights on the track are out and both screens cut off the light carried on the train causing both cells to be de-energized, current to be cut off, and a full emergency brake application to be made.

It is necessary for the driver to be alert and observe the signals. If he fails to stop before a signal at danger, the automatic control not only stops the train as described, but also blows a fuse which puts the automatic controls out of action. The driver must then proceed using the manual controls, and it is apparent that he has passed a signal at danger.

It will be noticed that the automatic control of the train is not continuous, as in other systems. It is thought that if all trains are of the same type with braking and accelerating relays exactly adjusted to the same value, the speed of all trains will be the same at every point on the line and the distance between them will not greatly vary. The safeguard against a train approaching one in front too closely for safety is provided by the lineside signals and by the vigilance of the driver who can revert to manual operation merely by moving his control handle from the neutral position.

By February 1, 1965, over 700,000 km (437,500 miles) had been run by automatic trains since June 1964 without any incident and with very satisfactory results. The consumption of electrical energy had decreased by over nine per cent and the appearance of flats on the wheels caused by heavy braking has completely ceased.

The F.C. Metropolitano has plans for seven short extensions in the very near future and work has already started on an extension of Line 2, northwards from Vilapiscina for ¾ km. Line 1 is to be extended 2½ km from Fabra-y-Puig and for nearly 2 km as a branch westwards from Sans. A further link of 3⅓ km is planned between Fernando on Line 3 and Plaza de Espana on Line 1, and by 1966 it is hoped to have built 7 km (4½ miles) of double tunnel to connect Sans and Sagrera on Line 1 via Diagonal on Line 3 and Provenza on the Sarria Line. There are 16 km (10 miles) of construction envisaged in these plans and many new lines on the drawing board.

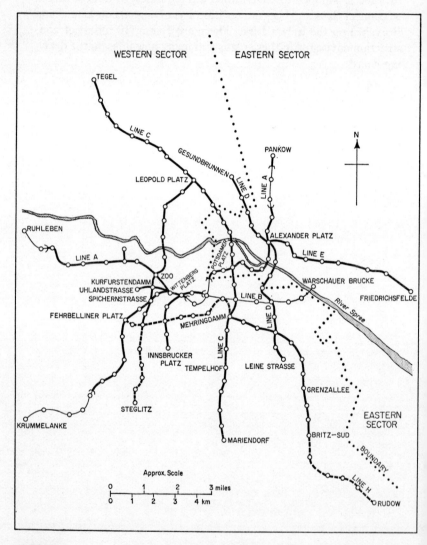

BERLIN

Berlin

In the nineteen-thirties the hub of the city was around the Unter den Linden and Potsdamer Platz, but this area is now in the eastern sector and only slowly recovering from the devastation of bombing and street fighting. The western sector has been rebuilt with a well-planned system of wide streets around the Kurfursten-dam and there is little traffic congestion, largely because the use-fulness of private cars is limited by the ban upon journeys into the surrounding country, beyond the borders of the western sector.

The B.V.G. (the Berliner Verkehrs-Betriebe) operates the bus, tram, trolleybus and underground services in the three western sectors, and there is a similar organization for East Berlin. Each organization owns and operates the fixed equipment of the under-ground in its own area, but the rolling stock is shared and at the frontier trains are exchanged, a westbound train being held by the East German authorities until they receive an eastbound train.

The underground system is exceptional in that it is built to two different tunnel gauges and sizes of rolling stock. The 89 route km ($55\frac{1}{2}$ miles) of the whole system are almost exactly divided between the 'small' lines, A and B, which run east and west, and the 'large' lines, C, D, and G, which run north and south, and E which runs east and west but is entirely in the eastern sector.

Small Line A runs from Ruhleben in the west and Krummel-anke in the south-west to a junction at Wittenbergplatz, whence it passes under the centre of the city, enters the eastern sector near Potsdamer Platz and turns north to Pankow. The total route length is about $19\frac{1}{2}$ miles, of which 5 miles are in the eastern sector.

Small Line B, from Innsbruckerplatz in the south and Uhland-strasse in the west runs to Warschauer Brucke to the east, just across the river Spree, half a mile within the eastern sector, and has a route length of 7 miles. This is the oldest line, dating from

1902, and only 1½ miles is in tunnel, the remainder being mainly on steel viaduct.

The Large Line C runs from Tegel in the north for 5½ miles in the western sector, crosses into the eastern sector for 2 miles and finishes at Mariendorf in the south, a total length of about 12½ miles. A former branch of this line from Mehringdamm to Grenzallee and Britz-Sud is now part of Line H.

Large Line D starts at Gesundbrunnen, ¾ mile within the western sector, crosses to the eastern sector for 2¾ miles, and crossing the border again continues for 3 miles southwards to Leinestrasse.

Large Line E lies within the eastern sector for the whole of the 4½ route miles from Alexanderplatz to Friedrichsfelde.

Large Line G is the most recent, opened on September 2, 1961, as a link between Leopold Platz on Line C and Spichernstrasse on Line A, with interchange to Line B at Kurfurstendamm in the main shopping centre and again with Line A at the Zoological Gardens. Work is now in hand to extend it southwards to Steglitz which will add 3½ miles to the existing 4½ miles of cut and cover tunnel.

Large Line H is in operation over about 8 miles between Mehringdamm and Britz-Sud, the section previously known as part of Line C, and is under construction for about 3 miles south to Rudow and for about 3½ miles westwards to Fehrbelliner Platz on Line A with intermediate interchange stations on Lines B and G.

Of the whole 55½ route miles, 40½ miles are in West Berlin. The large lines are almost completely in tunnel but only about 17 miles of the small lines are underground. Thus there are roughly 21½ miles in the open and 44 in tunnel.

The 88 stations in the western sector are used by nearly 200 million passengers a year, and there are another 34 less used stations in the eastern sector. The peak of traffic extends over rather longer periods than in most cities, from about 6.00 to 8.30 a.m. and from 4.30 to 6.30 p.m. and there is no midday increase in traffic, but at week-ends there are heavy loadings to the wooded countryside around the Tegelsee in the north and Grunewald in the south-west.

Trains of up to eight cars run at intervals as small as one and a half minutes in the peak hour at a scheduled speed of 33 km/hr

(21·25 m.p.h.) on the older lines where the stations are widely spaced, and at 30 km/hr (18·5 m.p.h.) on the new lines with closer station spacing.

Except on the old Line B where there are side platforms, the standard is an island platform 80 m (262 ft) long on older portions, and 110 or 120 m (361 or 394 ft) long on the newer sections. The newer platforms are about 23 ft wide with a line of columns down the centre supporting a sub-surface booking hall. Over the system the layout of the stations is very varied but, owing to the shallow nature of the tunnels, stairways are sufficient and there are no escalators.

Heavy snowstorms in the winter have led to the protection of stairways from the street against flooding, by pits about 4 ft deep beneath gratings 4 ft wide, and extending across the width of the stairway, usually about 8 ft.

The platforms of the new stations have false ceilings, which rise from the columns towards the platform edge, sinking again over the tracks, and with the use of a light pastel blue paint, this gives an impression of spaciousness. The platform walls are lined either with highly glazed hollow tiles about 10 in deep and 4 in wide, as at Hamburg, or with a sprayed mosaic of ceramic material in clear shades of blue, yellow or white, and highly glazed. Asphalt is used for platform surfacing, but the booking halls have floors of terrazo slabs.

The lighting is provided by fluorescent tubes in plastic shades and has an intensity of $3\frac{1}{2}$ to 4 foot-candles at platform edge. Emergency lighting from batteries can provide a dim light for a short while.

The stations are well kept and very clean. There is no necessity for washing down, but vacuum cleaning is adequate, probably because of the absence of the iron dust produced on some other systems from metallic brake blocks.

On both large and small lines the track gauge is 1·435 m (4 ft $8\frac{1}{2}$ in) and the 41 kg/m ($82\frac{1}{2}$ lb/yd) flat-bottom rails are 18 m (59 ft) long welded by the thermit process into 126 m (413 ft) lengths. Steel clips bolted to steel baseplates fasten the rails, and the baseplates are fixed by screwspikes to timber sleepers laid in ballast. On the main lines the maximum gradient is 1 in 25, and the sharpest radius 74 m (243 ft) but in sidings the radius may be as small as 50 m (164 ft).

The third rail is of 40 kg/m (80 lb/yd) section and is not welded. Top contact is used on the small lines but on the large lines underside contact is the rule, and the conductor rails are protected by planking.

The 780 V d.c. traction current is drawn from older substations with rotary convertors, and new ones with rectifiers, all fed from the ring mains of the Bewag Electricity Authority at 6 kV for the older and 30 kV for the newer substations.

Signalling is conventional with automatic colour light signals and trainstops. Three home signals are the normal provision.

Berlin is built in the marshy Spree basin upon a subsoil of sand and gravel capable of carrying massive buildings, but with a high ground water level, from 5 m on the north bank to 2 m below the surface in places on the south side of the river. The older tunnels were all built below the streets by the cut and cover method, causing considerable disturbance of the surface traffic, and necessitating elaborate provision of pumps in boreholes, to lower the water level during construction, and waterproof linings, as in Hamburg.

In general the tunnels are box shaped, in concrete with or without a central support between the two tracks. The large line tunnels are 6·9 m (22 ft 8 in) wide and 3·6 m (11 ft 10 in) from rail level. The small line tunnels are 6·25 m (20 ft 6 in) wide and 3·4 m (11 ft 2 in) high.

The rolling stock fleet comprises about 500 motors and 400 trailers of several different types. The older stock on the small lines is from 12 to 12·5 m (39 ft 4 in to 41 ft) long and 2.25 m (7 ft 5 in) wide with two separate doors on each side. The latest rolling stock, on the large lines, is 15·5 m (50 ft 10 in) over the body with a width of 2·65 m (8 ft 8 in) and three double doors on each side providing openings of 0·965 m (3 ft 2 in). These doors are opened by passengers releasing a catch and starting to slide them until compressed air takes over and completes the opening. The guard closes them by compressed air.

The cars are of steel throughout with a welded skin of unusually thin gauge which is said to render the car body as light as one of aluminium. The seating is all longitudinal and accommodates 36 passengers. The driver's compartment has a hinged partition which can be opened when no driver is present, to increase the room for standing passengers from 110 to 118.

Lighting is fluorescent of 9·3 foot-candles at eye level and 3·7 foot-candles at the step. Ventilation is reversible by air ducts and fans and heating is from the traction resistances.

All axles are driven, every bogie having one fully suspended motor mounted longitudinally midway between the axles driving each by a cardan shaft. Braking is rheostatic and with all axles motored it is used to bring the train to absolute rest. Emergency braking and holding at rest is by discs upon which caliper blocks are operated by compressed air. Springing is by rubber, using inclined blocks which are in both compression and shear.

The driver's control incorporates a knob which must be depressed for current to be on, and a miniature lever which is set against a scale marked in km/h. This lever controls the maximum speed up to which acceleration is automatic when current is switched on by means of the knob. A similar lever controls the braking. The first position operates the holding (air and disc) brake, four other positions provide four rates of rheostatic braking, and finally there are settings for normal braking by air and a full emergency air application.

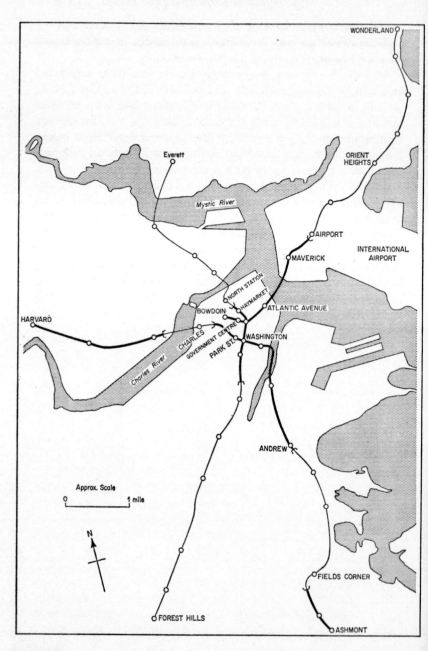

WONDERLAND

ORIENT
HEIGHTS

Everett

Mystic River

AIRPORT

MAVERICK

INTERNATIONAL
AIRPORT

NORTH STATION

HAYMARKET

BOWDOIN

ATLANTIC AVENUE

HARVARD

Charles River

CHARLES

GOVERNMENT CENTRE

PARK ST.

WASHINGTON

ANDREW

Approx. Scale

0   1 mile

N

FIELDS CORNER

FOREST HILLS

ASHMONT

BOSTON

Boston

The second most important port on the Atlantic seaboard is a compact city of 700,000 inhabitants which retains a very English character, with narrow streets, in the middle of a densely populated area. The Metropolitan Transit Authority serves an area of 5½ by 4½ miles, in which nearly 1½ million people live and work, but its system of underground and elevated railways, street cars and buses, has kept pace with the threat of crippling congestion. In eight years the number of vehicles in the Authority's car parks has doubled, to over a million, and perhaps their success may be judged by the proposals of two major railways to eliminate nearly all their commuter services to the city.

In June 1947 the Boston Municipal Transport Authority was established and in August 1949 had absorbed all public transport, including three lines which run underground through the city but are elevated in the suburbs. These three have a route mileage of about 23·5 miles, including 9·5 miles of tunnel.

The Boston Municipal Transport Authority was taken over in 1964 by the Massachusetts Bay Transport Authority to co-ordinate traffic over a wider area.

The Cambridge–Dorchester Line is 9 miles long. From Harvard Square, in Cambridge, there are 2·5 miles underground until the line rises to cross the Charles River on Longfellow Bridge and to run as an elevated railway for a further 675 ft. It then runs in the Dorchester tunnel for nearly 3 miles under Beacon Hill, the city centre and the harbour to a point east of Andrew Station, whence it continues on the surface, over a former steam railway, before going underground again for the last 4500 ft to Ashmont. There are three underground stations in the Cambridge Tunnel, with platforms 280 ft long, and five in the Dorchester tunnel with 350-ft platforms. Trains of 4 cars are run at 2½-minute intervals in the peak hours, and trains of 2 cars at 5-minute intervals in the slack period, at an overall speed of 21 m.p.h. The line is signalled for 35 trains an hour.

'The Elevated', between Everett and Forest Hills, passes through the city centre in the Washington Tunnel, which is 1·23 miles long and contains four stations with platforms 350 ft long. The elevated sections to the north and south add a further $7\frac{1}{4}$ route miles and are noteworthy for the Charlestown Bridge over the Charles River, which has a 240-ft swinging span, and the Mystic River crossing by a bascule bridge of 75 ft span. There are 11 stations on the elevated sections. Trains are of 6 cars in the peak hours with a $2\frac{1}{2}$-minute headway, and of 4 cars with a 6-minute headway in the slack hours, and the scheduled overall speed is $16\frac{1}{2}$ m.p.h. The line is signalled for 40 trains an hour.

The East Boston Tunnel Line runs underground from Bowdoin, in the centre of the city, to half a mile beyond Maverick over a distance of 2 miles, with an exceptionally long run of 4500 ft under the harbour between Atlantic Avenue and Maverick stations. Beyond Maverick it continues on the surface past the airport for 4 miles to Wonderland on Revere Beach. Two-car trains operate at $5\frac{1}{2}$-minute intervals, increased to 4 cars every $2\frac{1}{2}$ minutes in the rush-hour, and the overall scheduled speed is 20 m.p.h.

The Cambridge–Dorchester Line was opened from Harvard Square to Park Street in March 1912, to Washington in April 1915, and on to Andrew, station by station, in 1916, 1917 and 1918. From Andrew it went to Fields Corner in November 1927, and to Ashmont in August 1928. Charles Station was not built until February 1932.

'The Elevated' was opened as an elevated railway on June 10, 1901, using a tunnel which had been built in 1898 for street cars until in 1908 the Washington tunnel was built under a parallel street. Thus Boston claims the earliest underground railway in the Western hemisphere.

The East Boston Tunnel Line under the harbour from Government Centre, previously called Scollay Square, to Maverick was completed in the last days of 1905, and the line was not extended to Harvard Square until March 1916. This was used by surface type trolley cars up to April 1924, when a third rail train service was introduced. The line was extended from Maverick to Orient Heights on January 5, 1952, and to Wonderland on June 19, 1954.

The subsoil of Boston is clay with some patches of sand and gravel, and the tunnels are all shallow, of rectangular or arched

34

reinforced concrete construction, except for the Dorchester Tunnel. Under the harbour this is in twin tubes of steel about 24 ft in diameter and lined with concrete to give a final diameter of 18 ft 8 in. The tubes are close together with only 5 ft between them.

The remainder of the Dorchester Tunnel is of reinforced concrete with an arched roof spanning between walls 28 ft apart and reaching 17 ft 9 in above the rail level of the double track. The Cambridge Tunnel is also a double-track, reinforced concrete structure with walls 25 ft apart, in part with a flat roof 14 ft 9 in above rail level, and in part an arched roof 17 ft 2 in above rail level.

The older section of the East Boston Tunnel is a horseshoe-shaped concrete structure with a curved invert, 23 ft 8 in wide and with a maximum height of 17 ft 8 in from rail level. The newer section from Government Centre to Bowdoin consists of a rectangular tunnel in reinforced concrete with heavy steel beams in the roof and a flat invert. The dimensions are 28 ft by 14 ft from rail level.

The tracks in all tunnel sections, including the tubes, are ballasted. The running rails are 85 lb/yd flat-bottomed type set upon resilient pads and steel baseplates spiked to 6 × 6 in timber sleepers 8 ft long. On curves of the Cambridge–Dorchester Line and 'The Elevated' the rail is 100 lb/yd. The track gauge is 4 ft 8½ in and the minimum main line radius is 400 ft though in sidings it is as low as 75 ft. The maximum gradient is 1 in 20.

The third rail system at 600 V d.c. with top contact upon 85 lb rails, carried by porcelain insulators on extended sleepers, is used everywhere except over the East Boston Tunnel Line extension from Maverick to Wonderland, where an overhead system is used.

The signalling is on the automatic block principle employing three aspect colour lights with trainstops. Speed controlled approach signalling is used. A white light displayed below a yellow indicates that a signal ahead is showing the stop aspect because of a compulsory speed reduction, and it will not clear until released by a timing relay.

'The Elevated' is operated by 102 cars each equipped with two 120-h.p. motors, and 116 cars each with two 175-h.p. motors, one bogie carrying both motors and one bogie not motored. Each car is a complete unit and can be used singly or made up into a train of any number of units.

The East Boston Tunnel Line rolling stock consists of 48 motor cars powered by four motors of 40-h.p. and 40 cars with four motors each of 55-h.p. These are equipped to operate in 2-car units with only one driver's cab.

The newest cars of the Cambridge–Dorchester Line delivered in 1963 seat 56 passengers with 266 standing. The seating is longitudinal on glass fibre reinforced frames and stanchions and arm rests and other interior fittings are in stainless steel with a satin finish. There is practically no paint visible in the interior, which is lined throughout with laminated plastic in shades of blue, and even the window frames are made of an extruded thermo-plastic in a blue-grey colour. The exterior has been treated with an epoxy primer and finished with a spray of acrylic lacquer in blue, white and gold.

Heating is by waste heat from the rheostats of the motors to the extent of 60 kW and auxiliary heaters provide an additional 20 kW as required. A transistorized thermostat controls the heating and the ventilation given by six axial flow fans.

The cars are constructed of cor-ten, a rust-resistant high-tensile steel and weigh only 70,000 lb compared with over 85,000 lb for the previous type. They are only a few inches longer, at 69 ft 6 in over the body and have the same threshold width of 9 ft 6 in but the sides curve to 10 ft 2 in above waist level to give additional passenger capacity.

Trains are made up of one or two units, each unit consisting of two cars, one carrying the motor generator and the other the air compressor. Each car is equipped with four motors of 100 h.p. driving the 28-in diameter wheels through a double reduction gear. The order for 92 cars was split between two manufacturers in order to compare two different designs of control gear. On 46 cars an automatic cam switch control with a static type current limit relay and voltage regulator is fitted, and a parallel motor-axle drive is used. On the other 46 there is a static cam magnetic control making full use of static components and a right angle drive from motor to axle.

The bogies have inside frames and bolsters of unit construction in cast steel with bolster springs below the car body. The main springing is by steel coils sufficient to carry the tare weight and compensated air springing to maintain a constant floor height under varying load. Rotary hydraulic shock absorbers are fitted for lateral control and friction snubbers operate vertically.

Acceleration is up to $2\frac{1}{2}$ m.p.h. per second and the rheostatic braking gives up to 3 m.p.h. per second deceleration. The final stop, or emergency braking, is provided by pneumatic brakes with composition shoes. The coupling provides for simultaneous connection of the electric circuits and air lines and consists of a hinged head manually operated.

The system will be greatly extended in the next few years, but this will be mainly on the surface or as elevated railway. The East Boston Line will be taken on from the Wonderland terminal northeastwards to Broadway in the suburb of Revere. The Forest Hills–Everett Elevated Line is to have a new underground section from Haymarket to Causeway Street in the North Station area continuing underground to the Boston Main Industrial Building and then over the Charles River to Charlestown where the service will work over the Boston and Maine Railroad, an extension of $5\frac{1}{2}$ or 6 miles. Finally, a service is to be run from the Washington Street subway over to the New Haven railroad to the Back Bay Station.

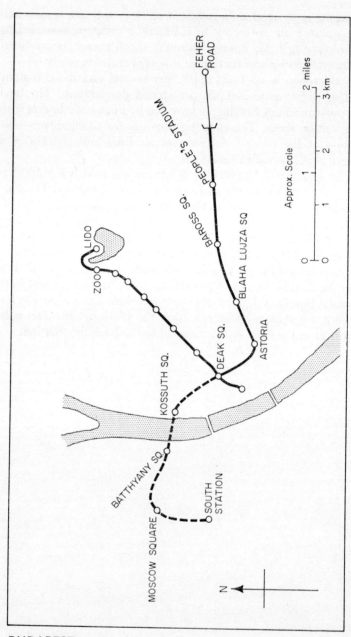

FEHER ROAD

PEOPLE'S STADIUM

BAROSS SQ.

BLAHA LUJZA SQ.

ASTORIA

DEAK SQ.

LIDO

ZOO

KOSSUTH SQ.

BATTHYANY SQ.

MOSCOW SQUARE

SOUTH STATION

Approx. Scale

0   1   2 miles
0   1   2   3 km

N

BUDAPEST

Budepest

The ancient twin city of Buda, on the west bank, and Pest on the
east bank of the River Danube, can claim to possess the oldest
underground railway on the continent of Europe. The Franz
Joseph Electric Underground Railway opened in May 1896, a few
months before Vienna opened her first electric tramway. In 1918
the Budapest Tramway Organization absorbed this Line, which
now carries quite light traffic in 19 tramcars running as single
units or, since about 1960, with a trailer attached.

The line runs from a station in the centre of the city, close to the
Pest bank of the Danube, north-eastwards along Andrassy Street
and the People's Republic Road to the City Park, where there is a
zoo, a permanent circus, a fun fair and the Szechenyi Lido for
swimming and sunbathing. The total length of 3·75 km (2·3 miles)
includes 3·25 km (2 miles) of cut and cover tunnel lying close
beneath the surface of the streets and containing two tracks. The
tunnels are 6 m (19 ft 8 in) wide and 2·75 m (9 ft 0 in) maximum
height from rail level and have a central row of pillars. Of the
eleven stations, nine are underground, only the Zoo and Lido
stations being on the surface.

The city has expanded very rapidly in the last twenty years and
the two million inhabitants make very extensive use of the existing
public transport, the number of journeys per person in 1960 being
640, compared with 519 in London. Soon after the war, plans for
a new underground were announced and construction started in
1950 upon an east–west Line of 10 km (6·25 miles). However, in
1953 it was realized that the country's resources of labour and
material could be better employed on housing and industrial
building, and the work was stopped. Material collected for the
underground railway works was actually used for factories and
houses and only maintenance gangs were left to maintain the
twelve tunnelling shields and to keep the tunnels dry so that they
could be used for storing foodstuffs.

When work ceased over 3 km (2 miles) of tunnel had been completed; 70 per cent of the running tunnels between the Stadium and Deak Square and over 50 per cent of the station tunnels were built, work having started at 8 station sites. The line was to be to the same lavish standards as those of Moscow and Leningrad with 5·5 m (18 ft) diameter running tunnels in cast iron and the same three-tunnel design of station with side platforms and a spacious concourse between them. Each of the three station tunnels is 8·5 m (27 ft 10½ in) in diameter and the platforms are 120 m (394 ft) long. With the two running tunnels generally spaced 20 m (65½ ft) apart, this gives an easy run into the stations. Acceleration and deceleration gradients are used at station approaches, enabling the line to be built at an average depth of 64 m (210 ft) without rendering the stations too inaccessible.

When the work was again sanctioned on November 14, 1963, it was with a more economical and utilitarian standard of finishings and with the use of reinforced concrete for some sections of tunnel. The use of the original shields has meant that the internal diameter of the concrete tunnels is reduced to 5 m (16 ft 5 in).

The first section runs on the surface for 1 km from Fehar Road and in a shallow reinforced concrete rectangular tunnel built by cut and cover methods for a further 1 km, which includes the shallow station at People's Stadium. The remaining 7 km and 8 stations will be in deep level tube. For 2 km, up to Baross Square and a little beyond, the ground consists of strata of sand and clay containing much water, and the tunnels were shield-driven under air pressures of from 1·5 to 2 atmospheres.

Baross Square station is at a depth of 30 m (98 ft) and while the lower escalator tunnel was mined in the conventional manner, the upper part was built in Baross Square inside a large caisson the height of a two- or three-storey building. The caisson was sunk into position complete with the reinforced concrete tunnel of 7·5 m (24 ft 7 in) internal diameter. This station is structurally completed and the appearance of the square is again nearly normal.

The most difficult construction area is around Blaha Lujza Square where the clay and sand contain inclusions of dangerously running sand, like quicksands. Here it is necessary to freeze the ground and to work in high air pressures. Work is in progress on this station and at the next, Astoria, where the station is being mined 30 m (98 ft) deep in a stable argillaceous soil. The concrete station tunnels are being lined with steel sheets welded together to provide a watertight skin. The escalator shafts have been completed, little remains to be done but the finishings, and completion was expected by the end of 1965.

Deak Square Station in good sound clay has been completed without the use of compressed air, at a depth of about 40 m (131 ft). This is the terminus of the first section which it is hoped to open by the end of 1970. There is a subway connection to the Nepkoztarsasag Road Station of the original line from Deak Square Station, and provision is being made for a future physical connection to the old line.

The second section from Deak Square to the South Station where the main line terminus is situated is already under construction. At the end of 1965 a start was made on driving the running tunnels north from Deak Square and under the Danube. The next two stations, Kossuth Square and Batthyananyi are not to be built until the running tunnels are completed. Moscow Square Station is about one-third completed and South Station is structurally finished but for 800 m (0·5 mile) of tunnel and the exits to the street. Work on these will be continued as labour is released from the first section of line. The soil on this side of the Danube, in Buda, is generally easier to work, though water was encountered near South Station and some blasting was necessary in rocky soil.

The line was planned to carry about 15 per cent of the passenger traffic of the busy central area, serving the busy east-west artery and the great housing estates in the Feher Road area. Trains are to be run at $1\frac{1}{2}$-minute intervals with three or four cars to start with and 6 cars when the traffic has grown to the expected level of half a million passengers a day. The overall speed has been estimated at from 30 to 34 km/hr (19 to 21 m.p.h.).

Experimental coaches were run for 25,000 km (15,500 m) over a test track in the People's Gardens from July 1953 and then stripped for inspection. These two prototypes were about 65 ft long, seating 54 with 186 standing, and each equipped with four motors of 120 h.p. (That the Hungarian works can build good rolling stock is shown by the fact that the original 216 cars for the Piccadilly Line, in London, delivered in 1906, were half

French and half Hungarian. The last of the Hungarian cars was taken out of service in 1930 after working since the First World War on the Aldwych Branch. It is interesting to note that originally the doors of these cars were operated by the guard using a wire rope and a winch.)

Probably because of the need to conserve national resources of labour, the line is to open with 80 cars, all motored, which will be built in Russia. Details are not available but no doubt they will be of a standard Moscow or Leningrad Metro pattern. They are to carry 170 passengers with a top speed of 90 km/hr (56 m.p.h.). Incidentally the escalators for this line are also to be of Russian manufacture. If the rolling stock has the same livery as the Hungarian prototypes, it will be attractive with cherry red sides, a brown stripe and butter yellow upper parts.

The whole system already proposed for Budapest consists of this first east to west Line, a north to south Line of about 8 km (5 miles) and a circular line to connect up the four termini of the transverse lines. Up to date authority has only been given for the preliminary planning of the north–south Line.

Buenos Aires

The capital city of Argentina, on the estuary of the River Plate, is the largest city in the southern hemisphere, with a population approaching four million. The province of Buenos Aires covers nearly a hundred and twenty square miles consisting largely of treeless plains inhabited by only about thirteen people to a square mile, but the city is the focal point of all the railways and the great port is the outlet for practically the whole trade of Argentina.

There are five double track underground lines across the city with 53 stations and a total route length of 28 km (17½ miles) serving some 400 million passengers a year. The oldest line, Line A, was opened in December 1913 by the Anglo Argentine Tramway Company and is still operated by British built rolling stock. Line B dates from October 1930 and used to belong to the Buenos Aires Central Terminal Railway. These two lines run directly from the dock area in the east to the main line termini in the west of the city.

The other three lines, C, D and E, were opened by a Spanish company between 1933 and 1944. Line C links the stations of the Central Argentine Railway at Retiro in the dock area with the Buenos Aires Great Southern Railway at Constitucion to the west of the city. Line D is from Florida in the dock district to the growing suburbs of the north-east, and Line E connects the main line at Constitucion with the eastern districts, running parallel to the old lines A and B, and carries less traffic.

The Buenos Aires Transport Corporation, set up in 1936, took over all these lines in 1939 but was replaced in 1952 by the Transportes de Buenos Aires, a specially formed section of the Ministry of Transport, and finally in June 1963 by the Subterranees de Buenos Aires. To integrate the lines into a single system has not been easy and it is still confusing to find the same name given to two stations on different lines, several hundred

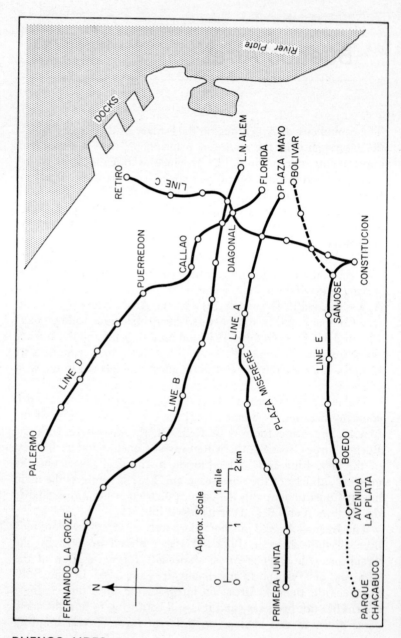

BUENOS AIRES

yards apart and in no way connected. The general pattern of four lines from east to west and only one making a cross connection is also very unsatisfactory.

Line A has a length of 7·25 km (4·5 miles) and 9 stations and is operated by an overhead system of 1000 V d.c. with 125 cars, each capable of carrying 150 passengers. The track conforms to the British tradition of bullhead rail, 45 kg/m (91 lb/yd) keyed up in chairs on timber sleepers and ballast. It is also the only line built by cut and cover methods with rectangular tunnels, 7·7 m. (25 ft 3 in) wide, without any central supports and a roof 4·45 m (14 ft 7 in) above rail level. At Plaza Miserere there is cross-platform interchange with the Domingo F Sarmiento (formerly the Buenos Aires Western Railway) broad gauge line which operates on a third rail system of 800 V d.c. and a track gauge of 1·676 m (5 ft 6 in) for about half a mile in a tunnel 9·3 m (30 ft 6 in) wide by 6·45 m (21 ft 2 in) maximum height. Incidentally, a second similar goods line of this railway runs parallel to Line A for 4·8 km (3 miles) to the dock area, but this is in single track tunnels 5 m (16 ft 5 in) wide and 5·7 m (18 ft 9 in) high.

Line B is parallel to Line A for 8 km (5 miles) with 12 stations but is operated from a third rail at 600 V d.c. The 76 motor units were made in America and each can carry about two hundred passengers. The track gauge is the standard 1·435 m (4 ft 8½ in) but has flat-bottom rails spiked down to timber sleepers on ballast. The tunnels were built by mining methods and are mainly rectangular, 8·45 m (27 ft 9 in) wide with a centre partition and 4·65 m (15 ft 3 in) from rail to roof, but part of this line has an arched roof over each track.

Lines C, D and E are operated by a fleet of 107 interchangeable cars mostly of German manufacture, but some locally made. The tracks are all of 1·435 m (4 ft 8½ in) gauge with 49·6 kg/m (100 lb/yd) bullhead rails in chairs and timber sleepers set in ballast. Line C from Retiro in the dock area to Constitucion extends for 4·5 km (2·8 miles) with ten stations. The tunnels follow the line of the streets above, although they were mined and not built by cut and cover; on the first section, Constitucion to Diagonal, there are curves of only 80 m (262 ft) radius but on the later section, Diagonal to Retiro, the maximum radius is 120 m (394 ft). The tunnels are of horseshoe shape, 7 m (23 ft) wide and 4·76 m

(15 ft 7 in) from rail to roof, and they only have thin inverts of 30 cm or about one foot of weak concrete below the ballast.

Line D extends from Florida, near Plaza Mayo in the dockland, north-westwards to the Buenos Aires Pacific Railway station at Palermo, a distance of 6·2 km (4 miles) and the very similar Line E runs from Constitucion on Line C for 4 km (2½ miles) westwards to Boedo. These lines do not follow the streets and it has been possible to avoid curves of radius less than 250 m (820 ft), except in one case where the radius is 230 m (755 ft) and, in this flat plain, the gradient can be kept below one in thirty-three. The tunnels of these two lines have straight walls and a high arched roof, with a width of 8·32 m (27 ft 3 in) and height of 5·36 m (17 ft 7 in). There is no invert, the ballast being laid directly upon the rail.

This absence of an invert is only made possible by the peculiar nature of the subsoil of Buenos Aires which is exceptionally stable even when waterlogged. Excavations are easily made with pneumatic picks and they require little or no timbering. Practically the whole 14·7 km (9 miles) of the three later lines was mined and only about five per cent was built by cut and cover, including the terminal stations at Retiro and Constitucion, Callao station and short portions under the traffic-free centres of squares. Shafts were sunk about 500 metres or a third of a mile apart, and pilot tunnels were driven along the line of the tunnel walls. The arched roofs were excavated, and only on this part of the work was timbering necessary. Walls and roof were cast in mass concrete before the central 'dumpling' was excavated and the floor levelled off to receive the ballast.

Where it was necessary to pass under buildings these were underpinned by building columns of concrete beneath the foundations to take the weight during excavation. When a short section of tunnel roof had been built the load was transferred to this and the temporary column was cut away from the interior of the tunnel. On Line D long stretches were below ground water level and it was necessary to lower this by about 4 m (13 ft) by pumping. At Pueyrredon station, in particular, water lay up to the springing of the arches, and waterproofing similar to that used in Berlin was necessary. Brick-on-edge walls were built and faced with two heavy layers of bitumen felt sandwiched in three layers of asphalt, and the mass concrete was poured against this.

For the cut and cover stations reinforced concrete was used with a flat roof, but the basic design of station is a single tunnel 13·4 m (44 ft) wide having side platforms 3 m (9 ft 10 in) wide and 106 m (348 ft) long. At important stations platforms are 4 m (13 ft 2 in) wide and a central platform is sometimes used, as at Pueyrredon where the station consists of two arches joining over pillars on the island platform. Generally there is a concourse above the lower station tunnel with stairs and escalators connecting them and the Retiro and Constitucion terminals have direct underground passages to the main line stations.

Each station, of the three newer lines, has a distinctive colour scheme with tiled floors and walls bearing large murals formed of tiles. On Line C these depict Spanish pastoral scenes and the tiles were imported from Spain, but the civil unrest interrupted this and for Lines D and E the tiles were made in Argentina and laid in Argentine motifs.

It is interesting that for Line C forced extraction ventilation was thought to be necessary, but for Lines D and E natural ventilation by the piston action of the trains has been found more satisfactory, although the invert of the lines is from 10 to 15 m, or 30 to 50 ft, below street level.

An extension of Line E westwards from Boedo for 1 km to Avenida la Plata, and another from San Jose north-east for 2 km to Plaza Mayo are under construction at the present time, and a further westward extension from Avenida la Plata to Parque Chacabuco, about 2 km, is expected to start in the near future.

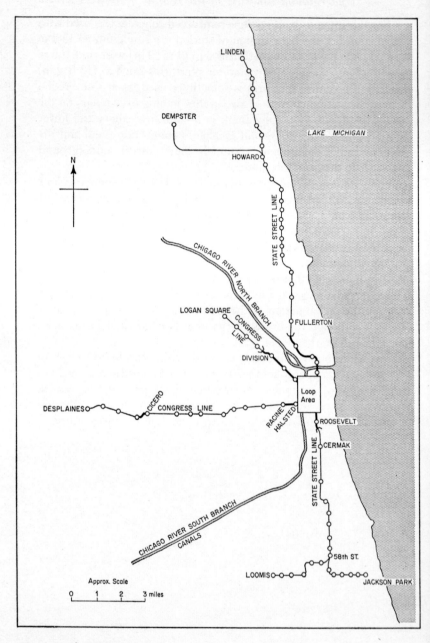

LINDEN

DEMPSTER

HOWARD

LAKE MICHIGAN

STATE STREET LINE

CHIGAGO RIVER NORTH BRANCH

LOGAN SQUARE

CONGRESS LINE

DIVISION

FULLERTON

Loop Area

DESPLAINES

CICERO

CONGRESS LINE

RACINE

HALSTED

ROOSEVELT

CERMAK

STATE STREET LINE

CHICAGO RIVER SOUTH BRANCH

CANALS

Approx. Scale

0   1   2   3 miles

58th ST.

LOOMIS

JACKSON PARK

CHICAGO (General)

Chicago

The wagon trains of the legendary West spread over the great plains after passing south of the great lakes, and the settlement of Chicago was the last rendezvous. In 1834 it was a town of 300 inhabitants, and within five years it was regarded as a city. Now it is the second largest city of the United States, a great railroad centre and port, and has a population of over 3½ million. From the city centre there is a peak flow of about 220,000 persons daily, of which some 140,000 travel underground.

The Chicago Transit Authority operates 73 route miles of urban railway, but only two lines go underground.

The State Street Line crosses the city in tunnel from north to south, and the Congress Line runs from the north roughly parallel to the State Street Line before turning off from the city centre to the western suburbs. These two lines carry about 120 million passengers a year.

The particular interest of this system lies in the continuous platforms in the Central or 'Loop' area of Chicago. On the State Street Line one island platform 21 ft 10 in wide and 3300 ft or ⅝ mile long, is connected by escalators to eight separate sub-surface booking halls. The trains stop at three points along the platform, the stopping points for north- and south-bound trains being staggered to avoid congestion. The Congress Line has a similar platform 2500 ft long served by six booking halls.

The State Street Line was constructed between December 1938 and October 1943 to form an underground link of 4·9 route miles between the north side elevated lines South of Fullerton, and the south side electric lines between Roosevelt and Cermak. An engineering organization was formed by the City Council especially for this work, but in 1945 this was superseded by the Chicago Transit Authority in order to take over the whole passenger transport of the City. The surface lines of the Chicago Rapid Transit

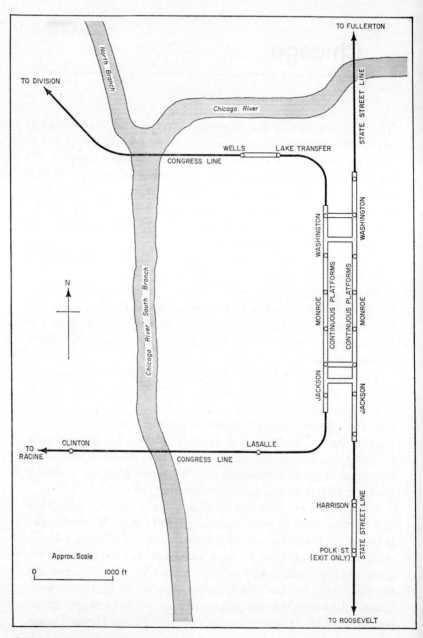

CHICAGO (The Loop Area)

Company were purchased in October 1947 and the Chicago Motor Coach Company's assets in October 1952.

Construction of the Congress Line started on March 15, 1939, and the first section was 80 per cent complete when work was stopped in 1942. It was resumed on March 25, 1946, and the line was opened between Division and a reversing loop at Lasalle in 1951, a distance of 4 miles. At the North end beyond Division it links up to the elevated tracks and the trains run out to Logan Square. From La Salle an extension in twin tubes was made in 1958 and trains now run in the median strip of the West Side Expressway for 6 miles to a point beyond Cicero. Then it swings out in twin tubes under the eastbound road of the Expressway, to a cutting between the roadway and the re-located tracks of the Baltimore Ohio Chicago railroad, and terminates at Desplaines. It is estimated that at only one-third capacity this line can carry more passengers in one direction than the four lanes of the Expressway at ultimate capacity.

The various surface and elevated lines connected to the underground sections operate services at quarter- to half-hour intervals and these combine to a total of about 25 trains an hour on the underground. The average scheduled speed over the State Street Line is 20·5 m.p.h. and on the Congress Line 21·5 m.p.h.

The City of Chicago stands upon a plain about 15 ft above the waters of the lake and from 4 to 10 ft above the original sandy loam of the prairies. Above the loam there is made up ground and below, at about water level, is a stratum of water-bearing soft yellow clay which runs when wet and shrinks when drying. Then 20 or 30 ft below water level the clay becomes blue, dense and impervious but still contains a great deal of moisture. From 60 to 70 ft below the lake water level there is a dry blue clay containing pockets of gravel and some small boulders, and at 80 to 100 ft limestone is found under the City centre. It was in the wet plastic blue clay that the tunnels were driven at a depth of around 40 ft below the surface, and compressed air was necessary.

To the north of the river the tunnels are of horseshoe shape with a heavy concrete invert. The arched roof section was first excavated from pilot tunnels and was lined with steel plates and curved steel joists over a distance of about 12 ft. A vertical cut was then made along the line of the side walls, and steel stanchions

51

inserted to support the roof lining and steel shuttering for the walls, while the tunnel area and the invert were excavated by hand mining. The invert was then cast and a 2 ft 6 in reinforced concrete lining was built, following up about 100 ft behind the excavation. The finished tunnels are 34 ft wide inside and carry a double track.

South of the river the clay was softer and there were many buildings with basements and rafted foundations. Therefore the two tracks are in separate tubes which were driven by shields. Each tube is built up with steel rings 33 in wide to an external diameter of 24 ft 9 in, and is lined with reinforced concrete to give a final interior diameter of 20 ft 5 in.

Beneath the river there was insufficient cover of clay for tunnelling. The approach tunnels were built in coffer dams and the actual crossing is made in two horseshoe tubes 200 ft long which were constructed as one unit in a dry dock and floated 18 miles to be sunk in a trench dredged across the river bed.

The continuous stations in the Loop area and other stations with island platforms were built by omitting the concrete from the adjacent sides of the tubes, placing steel stanchions and lintels and hand mining the intervening clay. A concrete arch for the roof and a concrete invert for the platform were then constructed, to achieve a triple arched station 58 ft wide.

The stations outside the Loop area vary in type, either with side platforms 11 ft 11 in wide or with island platforms generally about 18 ft wide and a little over 500 ft long.

In the Loop area the booking halls are sub-surface and to a standard design. They are rectangular, about 80 ft by 60 ft, and extend under the pavement on both sides of the roadway to provide access by steps to the surface from each corner.

They were built by the cut and cover method with floors 18 ft below street level, and a floor to ceiling height of 8 ft. From each of the two sides of the booking hall an escalator and a stairway runs down parallel to the direction of the roadway to the platforms, which are about 40 ft below the street. The escalators are therefore comparatively short, having a rise of 19 to 22 ft. They are reversible and have a capacity of 8,000 persons an hour, while the stairways are designed for 4,000 persons an hour. In all, the State Street Line has twenty-three escalators and the Congress Line seventeen.

The booking halls have a light grey structural glass on the walls in panels of 18 in × 36 in. These were delivered to site already attached to a 1·5 in concrete backing with non-ferrous clips for fixing to the walls. Ceilings are finished in white lightly tinted with green and the floors are of reddish brown concrete scored into a rectangular pattern. A band of white tiles marks the platform edge.

A method of assisting passengers to identify the stations has been fully developed from the Piccadilly Line in London, where the colour of the platform wall tiling was varied with this aim. Four colour schemes have been used for the platform areas, red, blue, green and brown. For instance, a red station, or train stopping point on one of the continuous platforms, has dark red painted columns with a light red arch and roof steelwork over it. The grey terracotta walls have incised lettering in bright red and both the illuminated and the plain signs are appropriately coloured.

The track is of 4 ft 8½ in gauge with 100 lb/yd flat bottom rails 39 ft long welded into continuous lengths up to 5700 ft by the Thermit process. In the tunnels, the rails are fastened by spring clips upon rubber pads $1\frac{5}{8}$ in thick inset into steel baseplates which are secured by four coach screws to red oak sleepers. These $6\frac{3}{4}$ × 10½-in sleepers are only 2 ft 6 in long and are set into the concrete invert at 2-ft centres, every fourth sleeper being 3 ft 10 in long and projecting to carry the current rail. On curves the sleeper spacing is reduced to 1 ft 6 in and again every fourth sleeper projects, but in addition every fourth sleeper, midway between the projecting sleepers, is a crosstie 7 ft 6 in long.

On the open sections ballasted track is used with sleepers of creosoted red oak, 6 in × 8 in × 8 ft long with the same 2 ft 0 in spacing on the straight and 1 ft 6 in on curves. On curves of less than 2300 ft radius, an outside check rail is fitted in special chairs on alternate sleepers. This consists of an 80-lb/yd flat bottom rail laid on its side with the upper quarter of its foot removed and the head projecting ¼ in above the running rail. The flangeway is kept correct by inserting shims as the rail wears, $1\frac{7}{8}$ in for curves of over 650 ft radius and 2 in for sharper curves. The minimum radius is 340 ft and rail lubricators are extensively used.

The single conductor rail is of 144 lb/yd section, in 40-ft lengths on straight track and 36 ft on curved track, to suit the sleeper spacing and is fishplated with four bolts and with welded copper bonds at the joints. It is carried on porcelain insulators on the sleepers. These rails are 6 in deep and of rather harder steel than the usual conductor rail in order to decrease wear at the expense of conductivity. Contact is on the head of the rail which is laid vertically.

At 1000 ft intervals the rails have feeder cables connected and the running rails used for negative return current are connected to return cables at 400 ft intervals. The 600 V d.c. supply is taken from substations owned and operated by the Commonwealth Edison Company and fed from their 120/208 V three phase system, which is used direct for lighting and ancillary services.

The signalling is by automatic three-aspect colour light signals, electro-pneumatic trainstops and single rail track circuits, one running rail being reserved for signalling and the other for the traction current return. Speed-controlled approach signals are used and there is a capacity of 40 trains an hour. The whole signal system is supervised by line supervisors who are in direct telephone communication with station staffs and loudspeakers on the platforms, and are in turn supervised from a central office. Punched tape programme dispatchers are used extensively.

For the whole system there is a fleet of about 1150 cars, practically all of modern construction. The exterior roof is red, down to the waist level is grey, and below this is maroon. The interior has a white ceiling and other finishings in grey.

The latest 180 cars have aluminium bodies on steel underframes, and glass-reinforced plastic ends. The large windows, about 3 ft by 4 ft are glazed with laminated safety glass tinted to cut down glare. The fluorescent lighting gives 25 to 30 foot candles at the reading plane, and the blue vynil fabric seats, 3 in wider than in earlier cars, are set transversely to seat 47 in one and 51 in the other car of each two-car set. Two pairs of doors on each side give openings of 4 ft with a central post intended to segregate passengers entering and alighting.

An air conditioning unit maintains the temperature in each car at 72°F. and relative humidity at 50 to 55 per cent with a crush load and exterior temperature at 95°F. Air is drawn from louvres

Plate 9 BARCELONA *A type 600 (1959) motor car of the Metropolitano Line 2.*

Plate 10 BARCELONA *Interior of a type 400 (1958) coach of Line 2. Of utility standard and de-gned for short distance travellers who do not mind standing, it nevertheless has a clean, neat appearance.*

Plate 11 BARCELONA *The unique system of automatic train driving employs the screen shown in t*
photograph between the rails. This interrupts the light from the lamp carried on the train, which can
seen in the centre of the picture, and de-energizes the photo-electric cell on one side or the other, caus
operation of relays in the control circuits of the train.

Plate 12 BARCELONA *Cataluna, the terminus of the Sarria Line. Passengers board trains from t*
side platforms and leave by the centre platform and the escalators at the far end. The geometrical decor
tion of the arches is a typical feature of these stations.

Plate 13   BERLIN *A modern train of 'large' type D stock on Line C. The false ceiling of the station, rising above the tracks and the transverse lighting tubes are a feature of the modern stations in this city.*

Plate 14 BOSTON A train of the newest (1963) stock on the Cambridge–Dorchester Line. The external sliding doors are an unusual feature of these cars.

Plate 15 BUDAPEST *Concrete tunnel being constructed under 1·6 atmospheres of compressed air. The mist is a usual effect of using high air pressures.*

Plate 16 CHICAGO *A two-car train of the 'New Look' cars delivered in 1964. These lightweight trains ca travel at 75 m.p.h. on the open and elevated tracks. Each car is only 48 ft long and is designed to negotiat a curve of 770 ft radius at 35 m.p.h.*

Plate 17 CHICAGO *The Monroe station stop on the northbound side of the ⅝-mile long platform of th State Street Line in the central area. Trains stop at three points along the platform, but to avoid con gestion north- and south-bound trains do not stop opposite each other.*

Plate 18 GLASGOW *The leading end of a motor coach showing the shoes upon spring arms which collect current for lighting and also control the signals.*

Plate 19 GLASGOW *The underground never reaches the surface. A car is shown being lifted by crane, from the outer circle tunnel into the workshops, for maintenance.*

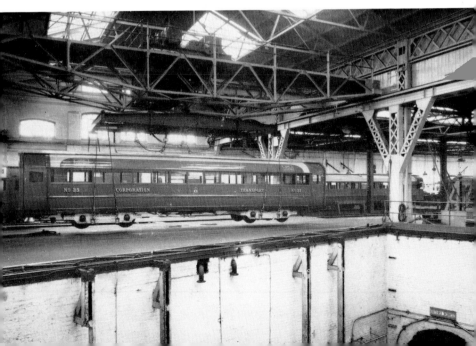

Plate 20 LONDON *The interior of a 1959 aluminium tube motor car on the Central Line.*

Plate 21 LONDON *Piccadilly Circus Station on the Bakerloo Line seen from the crossover between the tracks at the north end of the station, in 1954. The station now has fluorescent lighting.*

near the floor, filtered and heated and re-enters the car through grills at window sill level. Walls and roof are insulated with glass fibre.

These cars are 48 ft long over end sills, 8 ft 8 in wide at the floor, 9 ft 4 in at the waist, and weigh about $22\frac{1}{2}$ tons.

Service braking is rheostatic with disc brakes for the final stop and magnetic brakes on the running rail for emergency use. Each bogie carries two 100-h.p. motors driving through hypoid gears in an oil bath, providing acceleration of 3 m.p.h. per second up to 20 m.p.h., a balancing speed of 65 m.p.h. and a maximum of 75 m.p.h. Three acceleration rates are available to the driver, but an automatic interlock limits the performance when coupled to older cars. The control gear makes extensive use of static components, such as static converters, inverters and silicon diodes.

These 'New Look' cars (Plate 16) are the end product of ten years of research and experiment. The first trial of high speed cars took place in 1955 when four standard lightweight cars were specially fitted with new motors and controls to attain speeds up to 70 m.p.h. and each of the four was mounted on a different design of bogie. Again, in 1960, four more prototypes incorporating modifications dictated by experience were thoroughly tested before a final design was adopted. At the present time new cars run only on the surface branch to Dempster from Howard where there is cross-platform interchange with the Evanston route of the State Street Line. This five mile branch is being used as a laboratory to study the effect of a new service on employment and the use of land, building development and the level of rentals, street traffic and the attraction of passengers. This is the first project in which the transport operating authority has been financially supported by both the Federal Government and the local suburban authorities.

An interesting experiment is in hand with some wheels which have been made of aluminium and fitted with steel tyres. It is thought that the lightness of these wheels may reduce current consumption appreciably and it is also hoped that noise will be reduced. According to investigations made on the German State Railway, the major source of noise from wheels is caused by vibration of the wheel spokes or disc and the use of a more ductile material should reduce this vibration.

E

Finally, there is a unique underground freight railway which runs at about the same depth as the passenger system described above. In the construction of the latter it was necessary to re-build considerable portions of the freight tunnels which, following the centre line of the streets, not only crossed, but also ran along the proposed line of the passenger tunnels. This Chicago Freight Tunnel System has a total length of nearly 60 miles in tunnels 6 ft wide by 7 ft 6 in high. It carries over half a million tons of goods annually between the main line freight termini and individual factories and warehouses, using 125 electric locomotives and 2500 wagons running on 2-ft gauge tracks.

The Freight Tunnel System is invaluable in reducing the number of heavy lorries in the streets of the central area. There is already crippling congestion caused by the 20,000 private cars used in the peak hours which only carry 30,000 passengers or about 15 per cent of the commuters. It has been estimated that if all commuters were to use cars, 81 expressway lanes in each direction would be necessary and with parking space for all the private cars the whole central area would become one sterile desert of concrete and asphalt.

Glasgow

Glasgow was originally an ecclesiastical centre of learning, founded by St. Mungo in the sixth century, and the first cathedral was built in 1136. The earliest bridge across the Clyde was of timber, built in 1285 on the site of the present Victoria Bridge. In the Middle Ages Glasgow was a market town and not until the seventeenth century did the town council realize the advantages of enabling ships to reach the town. The river was then only about 10 in deep at low water; wharfs and walls were built, reducing the width so as to enable the river to scour the bed to a depth of 7 ft at low water and the city began its growth into the great commercial and industrial centre of Scotland with a population of over a million.

The underground railway consists of a single complete oval 6·6 miles in circumference, with 15 stations. It is unique in that the two tracks are enclosed in separate tubes and have no connections between them, and it shares, with the Waterloo and City Line in London, the distinction of never reaching the surface. All trains are stabled overnight on the running lines and for overhaul they are raised by cranes to the surface maintenance depot. The line carries about 27 million passengers a year in two-car trains at intervals of 3 minutes in the peak hour, and it takes about 28 minutes for the round trip of 6½ m giving an overall speed of 14 m.p.h. An experimental three-car train is also in service.

This is one of the oldest tube railways in the world and has an interesting history. In 1887 private citizens proposed a line from the north-west into the city centre to relieve serious traffic congestion, but the Corporation opposed this. A new plan for this loop line was approved in 1890 and it was first opened in December 1896, but closed again because of an accident, finally coming into service in January 1897. At that time trains in Edinburgh and Glasgow were worked up steep hills by cable haulage and the promoters adopted this method for their new railway.

Two 1500-h.p. steam engines continually moved a cable through 1700 sheaves between the rails in each tunnel. The trains each consisted of two cars, the leading one being fitted with a clamp which was tightened upon the cable to propel the train. The clamp was released when the train was to stop. This crude system worked at an increasing financial loss until 1922 and then the line closed down. The City Corporation purchased the line very cheaply, reopened it within a few months and began to consider electrification. In 1925 this was considered too costly but on reconsideration in 1932 an experimental length of 2000 yards of the main line was electrified. The inner circle was completely electrified by March and the outer by December 1935.

By 1934 the traffic had shrunk to 14 million passengers a year, and its recovery was delayed by the Second World War, during which a bomb closed the service for six months from September 1940. The peak load was experienced in 1953 with 35 million passengers.

The track gauge is only 4 ft and it was not easy to fit the comparatively large electric motors of those days into the small carriages, so one coach of each set of two was equipped with two 60-h.p. tramway motors on each bogie. A third rail system was adopted with d.c. at 600 V, but owing to the tight clearance at rail level it was necessary to set the conductor rail unusually high, at about axle level, upon brackets on the sleeper ends.

The use of steel sleepers prevented signalling by conventional track circuits, but ingenious use was made of the system by which cars were lighted by current picked up from a conductor mounted on the tunnel wall. This conductor was divided into sections and when a train was in a section, taking current for its lights, the signal behind was set at danger. This is supplemented by a mechanical device which puts a signal to danger when a train passes it, even if the lighting of that train has failed. Colour light signals are used and fitted with trainstops.

The 4-ft gauge track has 80 lb/yd flat-bottomed rails in 39-ft lengths continuously welded and laid on sleepers in ballast for three-quarters of the line, and in concrete for one quarter. Every fourth sleeper is steel, carrying the bracket for the conductor rail, and the others are 10 × 4½ in timber 6 ft long and spaced at 2 ft 9 in except at joints where they are 2 ft 6 in apart. The curves are

58

comparatively easy, never less than 660 ft radius but the gradients are as steep as 1 in 20 and 1 in 18 at the river crossing, probably as a result of designing for cable haulage. The 660 V supply is fed by connections to three of the tramway substations at Cowcaddens, Partick Cross and Shields Road stations and normally each feeds one third of the line.

Much of the subsoil of Glasgow is clay, but near the River Clyde it becomes sandy and water bearing. The running tunnels are all separate, of 11 ft diameter with a space of 2 ft 6 in to 6 ft 0 in between them, and the construction varies to suit the soil encountered. Cut and cover methods were extensively used and large portions consist of a ring of brickwork upon a concrete invert. Where rock was encountered it was blasted out and lined with brickwork. The maximum depth of the line is 115 ft; under the river it is 56 ft below high water level and it crosses in cast iron tubes, driven by shields in compressed air. The 15 stations have island platforms 120 ft long and 15 ft wide in arched tunnels of 28 ft clear span and connection to the street level booking halls is by stairs.

The fleet of rolling stock comprises 26 motors and 24 trailers, all 40 ft 9 in long 7 ft 8½ in wide and 8 ft 10 in high, weighing 17 tons 4 cwt and 9 tons 6 cwt respectively. They are painted red and seat 42 passengers longitudinally with standing room for another 42. Each motor car has four 60-h.p. motors, electro-pneumatically controlled.

The station and rolling stock lighting is taken from the public authorities' mains as a 440-V three-phase supply at every station. It reaches the trains through T-shaped conductors mounted in the walls of the tunnels, the lower, neutral, conductor being connected through the signal relays and the upper conductor carrying 230 V. The coaches have shoes, in contact with the conductors, carried upon spring-loaded arms (see Plate 18). There is also one circuit of 660 V traction current for emergency lights in every car.

The braking system is the Westinghouse air brake applied to all wheels. The air compressors also control the switchgear and the sliding doors at the ends of the car which are operated by the guard from the rear of the train. The guard can take current off in an emergency by short circuiting bare wires on the tunnel walls and then using a portable telephone set, as in London.

British Railways also operate two lines which run underneath Glasgow. The first is the Glasgow City and District which started to operate in March 1886 over two miles of cut and cover tunnel from a terminus below the Queen Street main line station, to Charing Cross and on towards Partick, Dumbarton and Loch Lomond. The second is the Central Low Level Line, an extension of the main line from the south roughly parallel to the first, opened in August 1896 over a length of about 3 miles, but with various branches adding up to some seven miles of tunnel. These lines were worked by steam but are being converted to the British Railway standard 25 kV, single-phase overhead system.

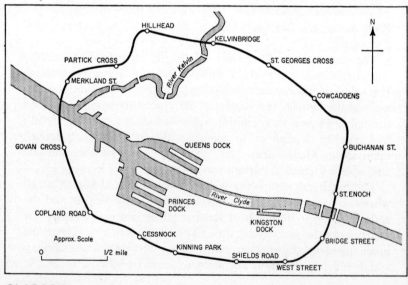

GLASGOW

Hamburg

Hamburg, with a population of nearly two million, is the second largest city in Germany and the greatest port. The docks on the River Elbe handle a vast traffic to the North Sea 85 miles away, from as far away as Czechoslovakia. Three-quarters of the city was utterly destroyed by bombs and, though it was largely rebuilt by 1955, the wide modern streets cannot contain the increasing surface traffic. Transport across the city is greatly hampered by the existence of the Alster Lake, a pleasure resort in the heart of the city. The Alster extends for two miles north and south and is up to half a mile wide with only one bridge across near the south end. In addition to the fleets of pleasure craft in the summer, there is a number of regular passenger services plying across and along the lake in launches.

Since 1937 the city's passenger transport, including the Alster boats, has been integrated in the Hamburger Hochbahn Aktiengesellschaft (H.H.A.) which is a public company with the city and state as controlling shareholders. The H.H.A. has a definite policy of replacing important tram routes by underground railways and the remainder by bus services, and to make their service so clean, convenient and comfortable, as to discourage the use of private transport.

The U-Bahn, or underground railway system, now consists essentially of a circle line around the Alster Lake and a north and south U-shaped line intersecting the circle at four points and connected to it at the north-east corner. The system now has 74½ km (46 miles) of route of which 20 km (12 miles) is in cut and cover tunnel, and this is all double track except for 7 km (4½ miles) of single track from Volksdorf to Grosshandsdorf in the north-east. Construction work is well advanced upon another line about 14 km (9 miles) long from Billstedt in the east, to parallel the other lines south of the Alster and crossing the circle at Schlump to run north-west to Hagenbecks Tierpark (Zoo).

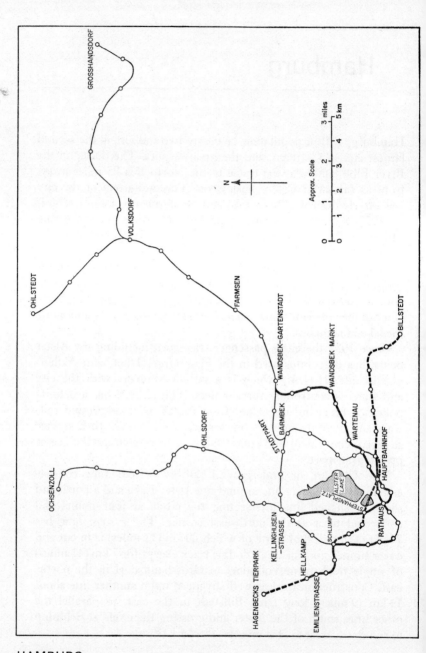

HAMBURG

The 66 stations serve over 170 million passengers a year who make an average journey of 6½ km (4 miles). From 4.30 a.m. to 1 a.m. on weekdays trains of six or eight cars run at a scheduled overall speed of 27½ km (17¼ m.p.h.) and at intervals of 2½ minutes in the peak and 5 minutes in the slack period. Through tickets are available for journeys partly by underground and partly by bus.

A strenuous effort is being made to render interchange between bus and U-Bahn easy and popular. The new Wandsbek Markt station exemplifies this policy. Escalators from the island platform of the railway give direct access to the bus station where the only booking offices are situated. The bus station is 384 ft long and 95 ft wide with 16 covered bus stops around it and a raised office in the centre for the bus dispatcher. This official has a view of all the bus stands and also an alluminated track circuit diagram to show the occupation of the station and approach tracks by trains. Each bus stop has an indicating signal with three aspects: 'Go' meaning depart on schedule: 'Wait' which shows that an approaching train is required to connect: and 'Go now' which authorizes the driver to leave ahead of time. When the 'Go now' indication is given the bus dispatcher will call in a spare bus parked in the road near by, or from the Wandsbeck bus garage.

Escalators are also installed at the Rathaus station where the Ochenzoll Line passes under the Circle Line at a depth of 15 m (50 ft) below the surface, but in general the stations are very shallow or on the surface and booking halls are usually at street level. The older stations are being modernized to the bright, simple, and functional architectural standards of the modern constructions, where the wall finish of mosaic patterns and high-gloss hollow tiles, 9 in × 4 in and 1¾ in thick, give an enduring and attractive appearance.

There are side platforms and island platforms 125 m (410 ft) long, but the latter are preferred as they lend themselves to one-man control. Except at terminal stations a single train dispatcher is on duty. At very busy stations, where there are side platforms, on older stations, and where a curve obstructs his view, the train dispatcher is equipped with a television screen on his raised stand. The camera connected to this periodically sweeps across the platform and enables him to signal to the driver when it is safe for him to close the doors and start. All trains carry only a driver, no guard. About half a train length beyond the station there is a flashing red light in the tunnel which the dispatcher can use to halt a departing train in the event of an accident to a boarding passenger.

The Circle is the oldest line, dating from between 1906 and 1912. Then the branch from Schlump was opened to Emilien-strasse in 1913, and on to Hellkamp in May 1914. From Kelling-husenstrasse, on the Circle, a line to Ohlsdorf followed in December 1914, and then the war halted development until on October 6, 1920, the branch of the circle from Barmbek to Volks-dorf was opened. This was extended to Grosshansdorf on November 5, 1921, and to Ohlstedt on February 1, 1925. Next, on June 2, 1929, the northern branch was taken southwards from Kellinghusenstrasse to Stephensplatz and farther on to Rathaus, again on the circle, on April 28, 1934. Finally, this line was linked up to Wandsbek-Gartenstadt in stages; to Hauptbahnhof on October 2, 1960; to Wartenau on October 1, 1961; to Wandsbek Markt on October 28, 1962, and to Wandsbek-Gartenstadt on August 4, 1963. Now some trains run on the Circle and out to Farmsen and another service runs from Ochenzoll through to Ohlstedt and Grosshandsdorf.

The Hamburg soil is composed largely of river silt and a fine black sand, with a high level of ground water. The normal method of tunnel construction is by driving piles to form side walls, lower-ing the water level between by pumping, and then excavating between the walls of piles. A reinforced concrete box tunnel is then built and the trench is back filled. The reinforced concrete invert must be heavily waterproofed and the side walls are placed by using a 4·5 in brick wall for external shuttering. This brickwork is waterproofed by a thick rendering of cement mortar, a layer of bituminous felt, one of corrugated aluminium foil and a final layer of bituminous felt. Similarly the roof is waterproofed with a multi-ply layer of felt and a screed of concrete above it.

All this involves great interference with the traffic of the street under which the tunnel is built, and recently the whole process has been speeded up by building up the tunnel of precast sections in 2-m (6 ft 7 in) lengths, lowered into a trench and jointed with a plastic compound. In sections close to heavy buildings whose foundations could be disturbed by flow of the soil as the water level was lowered, it was necessary to weight the bottom of the excavation with a layer of old rails up to 5 ft in depth. A particular case was the tunnel driven within about 6 m (20 ft) of the base of the tower of St. Peter's Church, which carries a steeple nearly 400 ft high. Where surface disturbance was impracticable, under the Circle Line and the main line railway between Rathaus and Hauptbahnhof, twin tunnels were shield-driven in compressed air, but this was an exceptional case.

Some of the older tunnels have an arched roof, but the modern construction is a reinforced concrete box 6¾ m (22 ft 2 in) wide by 3½ m (11 ft 6 in) high with a central support between the tracks. The short tube section of 270 m (886 ft) is in reinforced concrete tunnel of 6½ m (21 ft 4 in) diameter.

The track is of standard gauge, 1·435 m (4 ft 8½ in) throughout and is on ballast. The 37 kg/m (74½ lb/yd) flat-bottom rails are welded by the thermit or gas processes up to 450 m (1476 ft) in length from 15 or 30 m (49 or 98 ft) lengths. They rest upon timber sleepers with a simple baseplate and inverted U-shaped spring steel clips secured by coach screws. On curves and other sections where wear is heavy, bimetallic rails are used having a head twice as hard as the foot.

The third rail is of a heavy dumb-bell section supported in caliper-shaped insulators by steel brackets on the sleeper ends. It is arranged for underside contact and is completely protected by planking, above and on both sides, in the open and in the tunnels. The system works on 800 V d.c. For all but the newest stock, on which the lights are switched on by a photo-electric cell, there is an unusual system of light control. This involves the conductor rail being laid an inch and a half higher on the open sections than in the tunnel. When the shoe is raised to the open level the lights are automatically switched off in the train and the lights go on in the tunnel sections when the shoes are lower.

The rolling stock fleet consists of 624 cars. The oldest are some 30 years old but those retained in service are being brought up to date, the wooden seats, tungsten lights and timber body panels being replaced by modern fittings and upholstery with aluminium exterior panels. Most of the rolling stock is modern and of all metal construction in the form of two car articulated units, the

65

type D.T.1, of which 50 were delivered in 1958 and 1959, and the D.T.2 cars now being delivered. The 130 cars of type D.T.2 are of considerable interest but, perhaps, chiefly remarkable for the central common bogie fitted to many of them. In this form there are, in effect, two single-axle bogies joined together by a hydraulic coupling which can be separated in a workshop so that the two cars can be handled individually. These bogies also have a form of trailing link suspension which is unusual.

The units are driven by four tubular shaft motors each of 107 h.p. on the two end bogies and mounted on the cross members so that they can be detached and lowered into an inspection pit for servicing. The bogies are trebly sprung by rubber, with resilient wheels, rubber chevron springing of the axle box, and vertical bell-shaped rubber springs between the frame and the bolster.

The acceleration of 3·6 to 4·3 km ($2\frac{1}{4}$ to $2\frac{3}{4}$ m.p.h.) per second is maintained constant by an automatic control for varying loads, and wheel spin or 'pick up' is guarded against by an electronic device which adjusts the power or the braking if one axle starts to revolve faster or slower than the others.

The driver is only required to use his hands for the series–parallel switch and to sound the horn. Two rates of acceleration are selected by depressing a pedal with the left foot. The right foot operates a brake pedal giving three values of deceleration, and this also serves as a safety device. The pedal must be slightly depressed to release the brakes, and if fully depressed the brakes come on again. The degree of braking obtained is shown by coloured indicator lights on the control panel in the cab, a green light for the first stage, a yellow for the second and two yellows for full application. Service braking is at $4\frac{1}{2}$ km/h (2·8 m.p.h.) per second.

The maximum speed is 70 km/h (44 m.p.h.) but the driver uses the series/parallel switch to select a speed up to which the train will accelerate: 10, 30, 45 or 70 km/h. The initial stage of braking is rheostatic on the driven axles and by disc brakes on the trailing axles. The final stage, when the rheostatic brakes fade with reduced speed, or the emergency application, is by disc brake on all axles. The arrangement is such that the disc brake is applied by a spring which is always kept loaded by a battery-operated solenoid except when an emergency stop is required, traction current fails, the cars are uncoupled or a 'handbrake' application is required. There is, in fact, no handbrake but the disc brakes hold the train unless the driver's pedal is slightly depressed.

The D.T.2 cars run over the newest section of line between the city centre and Wandsbeck as eight-car trains each carrying over 1000 passengers and giving a line capacity of 24,000 an hour. Each car seats 82 on transverse seats and has four double doors on each side with clear openings of 1·214 m (4 ft). The two-car articulated unit is 28 m (91 ft 10½ in) long over the bodies, has a width of 2½ m (8 ft 3 in) and height above rail level 3·355 m (11 ft). The weight has been reduced to 35 tons from the 50½ tons of the earlier type D.T1. A saving of 0·8 ton is due to the absence of pneumatic brakes, 8·3 tons have been saved on the body, 3 tons on the motors and 3 tons on the bogies.

The bodies are designed as self-supporting tubular girders and both the body frames and bogies are welded structures composed of standard steel sections. The exterior panels of body and roof are of stainless steel coated with a clear lacquer. The doors slide externally and are painted light orange and the ends of the cars are similarly painted to ensure that men on the track recognize them quickly. Doors are opened by the passengers and closed electro-pneumatically by the driver.

The interior is finished in light-coloured plastic and great care has been taken to avoid dust-collecting ledges and corners. The seats are cushioned with foam rubber beneath a synthetic fabric. A continuous strip of fluorescent lighting is set over the advertising space above the windows, and the false ceiling is backed by glass fibre and paper honeycomb material for insulation. Fresh filtered and warmed air is introduced from ducts beneath the seats.

The main overhaul shops are at Barmbek on the circle, general maintenance and running repairs being performed in the depot at the adjacent station Stadtpark and in the spacious new depot at Farmsen which is over a kilometre long and designed to accommodate 340 cars. This depot is signalled throughout with 64 sets of points and 59 signals while from the control tower it is possible to set up 311 different routes. The control tower is linked for remote working with the three adjoining stations, Wandsbek-

Gartenstadt and Trabrennbahn to the south and Berne at the north end of the depot.

The S-bahn, a suburban surface railway operated by the Deutsche Bundesbahn (German National Railway), works in close coordination with the H.H.A. and is complementary to the U-bahn on the north bank. This is the only suburban railway connection to the south bank and the important residential and industrial district of Harburg. Half of the S-bahn is electrified on the third rail system and the other half, which is now worked by steam and diesel locomotives, is to be electrified on the D.B. system of 15 kV overhead a.c. when the main line electrification from Hanover is completed.

Kiev

Kiev, the chief city of the Ukraine, was virtually razed to the ground during the Second World War and has been rebuilt with wide roads and a wealth of open spaces and trees, but the new apartment houses extend monotonously for miles. The city is built on hilly ground around the wide meanderings of the River Dnieper whose sandy beaches are greatly used for angling and other restful relaxation; the river is busy with launches and a hydrofoil service for pleasure and travel to outlying buildings.

Plans for the Kiev Metropolitan Railway were ready before the war broke out, but construction was delayed until 1949. The first section of about 6 km (3·75 miles) and five stations was completed on October 22, 1960, and the first passengers travelled between the Terminus and Dnieper stations on November 7. A further 4 km (2·5 miles) and two more stations, Polytechnic and Bolshevik Factory were opened at the end of 1963. Work is now proceeding on a bridge over the River Dnieper which is to carry the railway and a road on separate levels to an island in the river and across to the new suburbs of Nikolsk and Socialist Town where a vast housing estate is to be built, with one apartment block designed to accommodate a hundred thousand people. At this stage there will be 13 km (8·1 miles) of route and 10 stations and already extensions to both ends are being planned.

The traffic already exceeds 30 million passengers a year and will increase greatly when the river crossing is completed. Trains of three cars run at present, but all platforms have been built 100 m (328 ft) long to accommodate five car trains. The service interval is 2 minutes in the peak hours and 2½–3 minutes in the slacker periods and with well-disciplined passengers completing their boarding and alighting in less than 30 seconds, an overall speed of 38 km/hr (24 m.p.h.) is attained. A flat rate fare system simplifies operation.

The city is particularly proud of the Metro stations which are intended to remain for generations as monuments to the culture and accomplishments of the first Soviet epoch and in this they resemble those of Moscow and Leningrad but have a typically Ukrainian style of decoration. They are washed down and scrubbed, tracks, walls and platforms, every day, and present a polished, litter-free appearance. In 1952 and 1957 competitions for the architectural design of stations were thrown open to all Soviet citizens and produced 82 entries of which six were chosen for the six underground stations. Each is intended to present a different aspect of Ukrainian culture and the materials were selected as much for durability as for their aesthetic appeal. A feature common to all is the 'Moscow' type of spacious central concourse, from 5·7 to 5·9 m (about 19 ft) wide and 5 m (16 ft) high. In the first three stations these are separated from the platforms by massive pillars 4·6 m (15 ft) wide leaving openings of 3·6 m (11 ft 9 in) for access.

Terminus station is part of the main line principal station but the Metro entrance is distinguished by portals of granite set in white limestone. A single flight of escalators leads down to a concourse built in marble and granite in imitation of the timber buildings typical of Kiev in earlier days. Decorative aluminium ventilation grilles carry eight bas-reliefs in bronze, each of about 2 m (6 ft 6 in) diameter depicting the main events of recent Ukrainian history such as union with Russia and the October Revolution.

University station is at the entrance to the Botanical Gardens, near the Schevenko University, and the entrance hall is designed to resemble a garden pavilion with a façade in light-coloured marbles and a roof in the form of a cupola 18 m (59 ft) in diameter formed of 36 reinforced concrete segments. There are two flights of triple escalators at this very deep station, with an intermediate hall which is very similar in internal appearance to the entrance hall. In the concourse the pillars are of pink Carpathian marble with niches containing busts of national philosophers, scientists and writers, and at the end there is a large statue of Lenin. The freize and cornice, and surrounds to the busts, are of a specially produced translucent white plastic which reflects the lighting from green glass shades on the cornice. The use of the pink marble of which the University is largely built is extended even to the walls of the platforms.

Plate 22   LONDON   *A Metropolitan Line train of the newest 'A60' stock.*

late 23   LONDON   *The concourse between platforms at Gants Hill. This was the forerunner of the*
oscow type of station.

Plate 24 LONDON *Welded rails 300 ft long loaded ready to go out from the depot where they ar*
welded from 60 ft lengths. This photograph was taken in 1952 and specially fitted wagons are now use
and fitted with mechanical means of loading up rails from the track.

Plate 25 LONDON *In the winter points are heated by this apparatus. Oil in the tank on the left is kept at a thermostatically controlled temperature by electric heating and is pumped through pipes and channels through the rail chairs to keep them free of ice.*

Plate 26 LONDON *In freezing weather de-icing fluid is spread along the conductor rails from this bath which replaces a section cut out of the rail. The rectangular tank is full of liquid which the train shoes pick up from the revolving roller.*

Plate 27   LONDON   *An iron lined tunnel of the Victoria Line, experimental section. Track is laid but signals and cables have yet to be installed.*

Plate 28   LONDON   *A concrete lined tunnel of the Victoria Line. The taper wedges which expand the rings against the surrounding clay can be seen at the top.*

Plate 29 MADRID *Interior of a modern motor car. The seating is meagre but the provision of grips fo[r]*
standing passengers is lavish, over windows, each side of doors, on seat backs and centrally in the car roo[f]

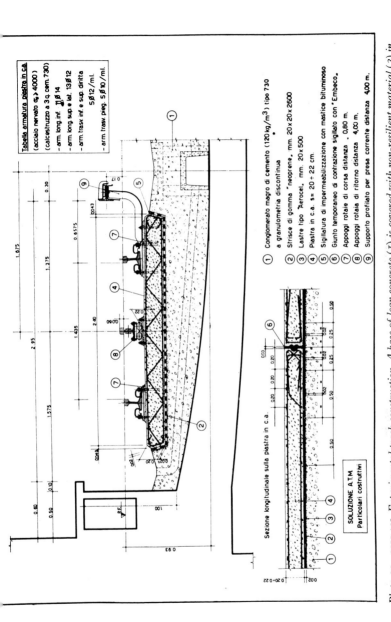

Plate 30 MILAN *Experimental track construction. A base of lean concrete (1) is covered with non-resilient material (3) in which there are synthetic rubber strips (2) to act as springs. The whole is then covered with a polythene sheet (5), and the reinforced concrete formation is cast upon it with expansion joints (6) at 12 m intervals.*

Plate 31 MONTREAL *The rock tunnel has been blasted out and is temporarily supported, over a short length of weak rock, before being concreted.*

Plate 32 MONTREAL *The bogie of a train in a maintenance shop, showing the load carrying and guiding pneumatic tyres, and the flanged steel 'safety' wheels.*

The booking hall at Kreshchatnik forms part of the Metro Restaurant and ceramic wall tiles of many colours imitate the random patterns characteristic of the traditional Ukrainian carpets. Panels set in the broad columns of the concourse also present this motif, but apart from an extensive use of majolica* and a large coat-of-arms of the Republic, the decoration is comparatively restrained.

Arsenal is the deepest station, with two flights of triple escalators reaching to a depth of over 100 m (328 ft). The intermediate hall is cylindrical with a domed roof. This was sunk into position from the surface as one bell-shaped unit 22·6 m (nearly 75 ft) in external diameter and 18·7 m (60 ft) high. The whole hall was placed by cranes in a prepared excavation 4 m (13 ft) deep and, as the ground was excavated, from within, the cylinder sank under its own weight. The excavated ground was passed down a vertical shaft into a horizontal gallery at the final depth of 50 m (164 ft) from which it was taken up a vertical working shaft alongside. The whole process took nearly four months but was completed five hours before schedule.

The concourse at this station is shorter than elsewhere on the line and has only two access passages to each platform, an inadequate provision for the rush-hour. There is a comparative absence of extraneous decoration on the light yellow marble walls; the floor is of pink granite and the fluorescent lighting is in a quite ordinary type of plastic shade.

The railway emerges from the hillside into Dnieper station which is built upon a viaduct that will form the approach to the new two level road and rail bridge over the river. It is an open-air station of light reinforced concrete construction with a profusion of glass. The side platforms are protected by a wide cantilever roof spanning 16 m (52 ft) and wide stairways lead down to the river bank as well as up to the street.

The two newer stations, Polytechnic and Bolshevik Factory have been designed to avoid the somewhat claustrophobic effect of the massive architecture of the earlier stations. Pillars have been reduced in width from 4·6 m (15 ft) to 1·55 m (5 ft) at Polytechnic and 2·25 m (7 ft 4 in) at Bolshevik Factory. Brilliant lighting is provided from concealed 'daylight' fluorescent tubes and the

*Majolica. Type of enamelled pottery originating in Majorca and developed in Italy.

decoration with pink marble and majolica is cheerful but not oppressively ornate. Polytechnic station is housed within the headquarters building of the new Kiev Metropolitan.

The equipment of the railway closely follows the pattern set by the other Soviet systems. The track gauge is 1·542 m (5 ft) and the flat bottom rails weighing 50 kg/m (101 lb/yd) are continuously welded upon sleepers embedded in concrete. The outside third rail carries 825 V direct current from substations which are remotely controlled from the traffic controller's office.

Signalling is by automatic block with colour lights and train-stops but automatic equipment is provided for reversing at terminals.

The rolling stock, based on the Leningrad design, has an overall length of 19·17 m (62 ft 10 in), four sets of wide double doors on each side and seating for 44 passengers with 220 standing. The cars are of all-metal construction and have a maximum speed of 75 km/hr (47 m.p.h.). Braking is rheostatic with pneumatic brakes for the final stop and for emergencies.

The running tunnels, of 5·1 m (16 ft 9 in) internal diameter are all built of reinforced concrete segments and are constructed on the 'hump' pattern, rising up to the station and falling away from it. This design was first used on the London Central Line to secure the braking effect of an upgrade in approaching a station, and the added acceleration due to a downgrade on leaving. The results are a reduction of brake wear and of accelerating current, but there is a disadvantage in heavy traffic conditions in that a train stopped or slowed at the entrance to a station, occupied by the preceding train, loses time by slower acceleration on the upgrade.

In the earlier construction, in 1952 and 1953 a form of skew-edged interlocking segment was used but presented some difficulty in erection, and in 1956 a design of straight right-angle edged segments was adopted. These are cast with semicircular grooves of 7 cm (2·8 in) diameter in the mating faces which are filled with cement grout after erection. The space behind the concrete segments is also filled with grout by injection through holes cast in them and the result is a completely waterproof tunnel. Each ring is formed of six segments and a key, 1 m (39 in) wide. The earlier segments were 30 cm (1 ft) thick and weighed 2·1 tons each, but as work proceeded it was found possible to reduce the thickness to 25 cm (10 in) and the weight of steel reinforcement from 630 kg (1390 lb) to 490 kg (1080 lb) per ring, with a resulting reduction of about 4 in in the diameter of the excavation.

Much of the tunnelling was through clay and dry soil. With a highly developed rotary digger, and well-mechanized means of disposal of the spoil, progress was rapid, attaining 200 m (650 ft) a month. However, considerable difficulty was encountered on the University to Polytechnic section. Near Terminus there is an old river bed of wet sandy soil and it was necessary to resort to chemical consolidation of the soil and to drive the tunnels 1·4 m (4 ft 6 in) lower than was intended. It was also necessary to use compressed air at 1·4 atmospheres in excavating the tunnels of Terminus station where the escalator shafts pass through unstable water bearing ground. The greatest hazard was met between Terminus and Polytechnic over a length of 250 m (800 ft) where there was only 6 m (20 ft) of cover of very weak ground. Here it was necessary to pump from the surface in wells to lower the water table and to use a pressure of 4 atmospheres to support the ground.

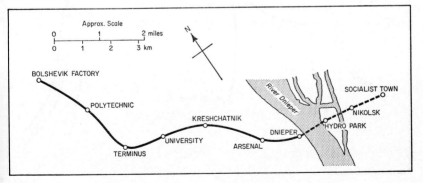

KIEV

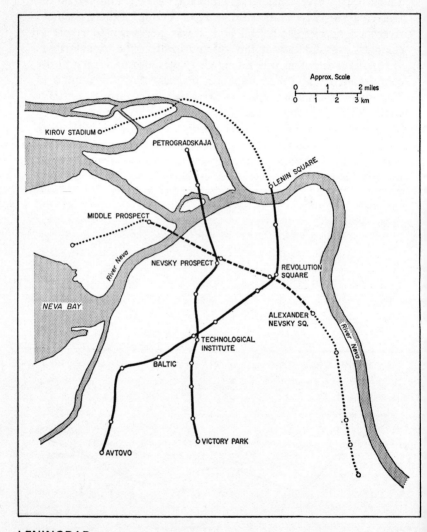

Approx. Scale

KIROV STADIUM

PETROGRADSKAJA

LENIN SQUARE

MIDDLE PROSPECT

River Neva

NEVSKY PROSPECT

REVOLUTION SQUARE

NEVA BAY

ALEXANDER NEVSKY SQ.

River Neva

TECHNOLOGICAL INSTITUTE

BALTIC

VICTORY PARK

AVTOVO

LENINGRAD

Leningrad

Peter the Great planned the central area of Leningrad and it remains an outstanding example of unified design with the palaces and other luxurious buildings proudly and carefully preserved. The centre of the city escaped almost unscathed from war and the classical façades of the large houses have not been spoilt in the process of conversion into flats. New blocks of apartments have covered the suburban areas that were devastated by siege and bombardment and with rapid industrial development the city's population is close upon four million, a figure exceeded in Russia only by Moscow.

Leningrad is the principal Soviet outlet to the Baltic sea, handling large volumes of cargo in the summer when the sea and canals are free of ice. The River Neva, half a mile wide, and the many branches of its delta and several large canals form barriers to surface transport, while the silty wet soil is not suitable for sub-surface tunnels.

The Metro is a simple system of two north–south tube lines across the city carrying more than half a million passengers on a weekday and considerably more on a Sunday. In all essentials there is a very close resemblance to the Moscow underground, with the same fare system designed to channel long distance travellers underground, and short distance traffic to surface transport, a tendency greatly helped by the depth of the tube stations. As in Moscow, a majority of the staff are female and even the remotely controlled substations are supervised by women.

The stations have entry barriers only which are normally open but immediately close if a light ray on the approach side is broken before the correct flat rate fare is inserted in a slot. As each passenger interrupts a light ray at a second barrier the mechanism is reset ready for the next. The Russian passenger is an orderly person and sufficient barriers are provided to ensure that the system works in the peak hour but no further development of automatic fare collection seems likely because it is expected to make the use of all public urban transport free throughout Russia during the next year or two.

Trains of 6 cars are operated at 3-minute intervals in the slack period and 2 minutes during the two peak periods each of about two hours, but all new stations are being built to accommodate 8-car trains. The comparatively long distances between stations enable a high overall average of 50 km/hr (31 m.p.h.) to be attained with the assistance of disciplined passengers and train dispatchers and the use of additional staff to reverse trains at terminals while the regular driver changes ends.

Construction of the system started in 1948 with the line between Revolution Square and Avtovo where the only rolling stock depot is situated. This was opened on October 22, 1955, and links the main line stations, Moscow at Revolution Square, Vitebsk at the Technological Institute and Baltic and Warsaw stations at Balticskaya with the large Livov Works. In 1958 this line was extended northwards to Lenin Square for the Finland main line station, giving a total route length of $15\frac{1}{2}$ km ($9\frac{3}{4}$ miles).

The second line between Petrogradskaya and Technological Institute was opened in 1960 and extended to Victory Park in 1963, adding a further 10 km ($6\frac{1}{4}$ miles).

A third line from east to west is now being constructed to open between Alexander Nevsky Square and Middle Prospect in 1967, and will be extended shortly thereafter at both ends. An extension from Lenin Square on the original line is planned to run westwards to open up an area of natural beauty and pleasure resorts and to end at the Kirov Stadium, on an island roughly 3 miles west of Petrogradskaya and about 5 miles from Lenin Square. In all it is planned to provide 116 km ($72\frac{1}{2}$ miles) before 1980.

The Neva Delta area consists of water-saturated sand and ballast, silt and limestone to a depth of about 12 m (40 ft) and below this the Cambrian clay contains numerous pockets of sand down to about 50 metres (164 ft). Consequently the tunnelling has been carried out in the sound clay at a depth of 60 m (200 ft) or more below the street level and where shafts have been sunk or escalator tunnels built, it has been necessary to use compressed air. The older line was built with cast iron linings, similar to those in Moscow but slightly thinner and lighter but after concrete linings had been perfected and proved in Moscow they were adopted for the later lines in Leningrad.

The tunnel diameter is 5·38 m (17 ft 6 in) compared with 5·5 m (18 ft) in Moscow, although the same size of rolling stock is used.

The stations follow the Moscow pattern with a central concourse and side platforms and considerable use is made of natural marbled stone for decoration. Some pictorial mosaics exist at the older stations, but the newer the station the less florid the decoration and the newest interiors are in good western, almost classical, style, but at the same time individually varied. As in Moscow, there is a striking clean line, absence of advertisements and clutter, and a clever use of fluorescent lighting.

The terminal station at Petrogradskaya is of peculiar interest in that there is a central concourse but no platforms. Passengers alight from the train directly into an opening from the concourse which is fitted with pneumatically operated doors. These openings are about eighteen inches wider than the train doors and the driver must exercise some care to bring the car doors opposite to them. There is insufficient room between the concourse doors and train doors for anyone to be trapped there and the concourse doors do not open until the train is at rest. This prevents passengers from falling on the track by accident or on purpose, and as it is a terminal station passengers are only leaving the train on one side and entering a train from the other side of the concourse, so that there is no opposing traffic. There is some saving in lighting and maintenance but the capital saving is great in doing away with the expensive, large, specially mined platform tunnels.

Another interesting feature is the elaborate system of protection against the heavy winter snowfalls, at Revolution Square. Outside the swing doors a vertical grille on both sides emits warm air to form a curtain in which snow will melt. Inside the doors a grating covers a pit, four feet deep, to collect snow from passengers' feet and clothing, melted snow which may drive in through the doors, and flood water in the spring thaw. Beyond this a flight of steps climbs five feet to the booking hall floor.

Escalators follow the pattern set by Moscow Metro and extend in one flight up to 60 m depth and, of course, are necessary at all

77

tube stations. They are run at the unusually high speed of 195 ft/min.

The track is laid with 50 kg/m (101 lb/yd) flat-bottomed rails welded into 200 m lengths (about 650 ft) and resting upon synthetic rubber pads and steel baseplates fixed to timber sleepers by steel clips and coachscrews. The sleepers are set in concrete with a drainage channel in the centre, as in other Russian systems and in London. The track gauge is, of course, the Russian standard of 1·524 m (5 ft 0 in). The single conductor rail, mounted by brackets on the end of the sleepers, is arranged for underside contact and covered with protective planking. The 825 V d.c. traction current is drawn from mercury arc rectifiers in an underground remote controlled substation at every station, fed from the City Electricity supply at 6 kV.

The signalling is automatic with colour lights and electromechanical trainstops, and comparatively uncomplicated. The layout of the lines include only a scissors crossover and two reversing sidings beyond each terminal and a central siding at the proceeding station. There are two two-aspect home signals and a three-aspect starter with automatic route setting into the sidings at the terminals and the whole can be operated from the central control room or by local manual control. An experimental programme machine is being experimented with but hardly seems necessary with such a simple layout. The third rail carries a telephone circuit for communication between the driver and controller.

The rolling stock is quite clearly based upon the Moscow pattern but has been improved by the use of lighter motors. Each bogie has two 120 h.p. fully suspended motors mounted parallel to the axles which are driven by flexible shafts and reduction gearing with a ratio of 1 to 5·79. The stock is designed for 75 km/hr (46½ m.p.h.) but is subject to a service restriction of 65 km/hr (40 m.p.h.) Rheostatic braking and acceleration are provided with load control and 18 notches for braking and 20 for acceleration. Automatic coupling is secured by a Schaffenberg type mechanical coupler and a 32-plug electrical coupler.

The rolling stock is maintained in a 12 track depot at Avtovo which accommodates 100 cars. Here there are cleaning pits equipped with compressed air for cleaning the underside of cars, with vacuum extraction; side platforms with hand-operated compressed air jets to clean inside and outside the cars, a hood which fits to within an inch of the roof to provide vacuum extraction of the dirt; and a soap and hot water brush washing machine. Cars pass through this cleaning process every five days.

Routine examination over a pit takes about half an hour and occurs after six hours' running. Electrical inspection and minor repairs follow every 3000 km (1860 miles) of service, and running repairs take place at intervals of 32,000 km (19,800 miles). Body lifting occurs at 200,000 km (124,000 miles) and complete over-haul after about 1½ million km.

It is, of course, necessary to stable the stock in heated sheds and a high-pressure hot water system is supplied from oil-fired boilers.

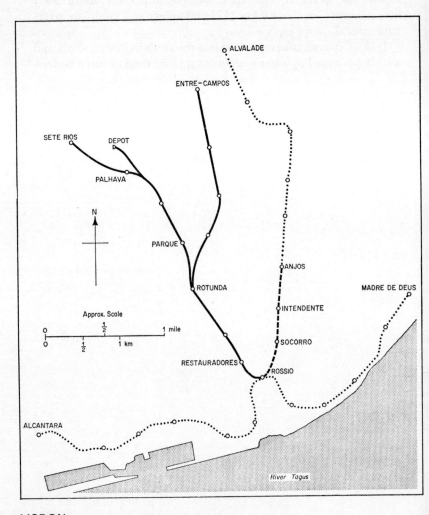

ALVALADE

ENTRE-CAMPOS

SETE RIOS   DEPOT

PALHAVA

N

PARQUE

ROTUNDA   ANJOS

MADRE DE DEUS

INTENDENTE

Approx. Scale

SOCORRO

0   ½   1 mile
0   ½   1 km

RESTAURADORES

ROSSIO

ALCANTARA

River Tagus

LISBON

Lisbon

Before the River Tagus reaches the sea it opens out into a magnificent landlocked harbour some ten miles long and up to five miles broad, surrounded by low hills. Lisbon, the capital of Portugal, lies at the seaward end on the north bank behind docks and quays stretching for 2½ miles. A small area, now the commercial centre, was rebuilt in block pattern after the disastrous earthquake of 1755, but the surrounding town of 800,000 inhabitants has grown over the years in a random fashion.

At present the Metropolitano de Lisbon operates a single route of double track from north to south with a branch to the northwest, but construction is in hand upon a second line which will continue the first from a U-bend at Rossio in the city centre, back to the north, parallel to the first. A third line to be built in the near future will follow the waterfront, turning inland for a short distance to give interchange at Rossio. Further plans include extensions to the first and third lines and a semi-circular link to connect all lines through the outer part of the city.

The Metropolitano Company was formed in 1949 and started construction in 1955. On December 30, 1959, the line opened between Entre Campos and Restauradores with a branch from Rotunda to Sete Rios and on January 27, 1963, it reached Rossio. Work is well advanced on the first section of Line 2 including three stations, Socorro, Intendente and Anjos. This will add 1½ km (nearly a mile) to the existing 7 km (4¼ miles) of route and raise the number of stations from 12 to 15. When the system is completed it will be 40 km (25 miles) long and will have 31 stations or more.

The line is entirely underground but only one station, Parque, is of sufficient depth to warrant the installation of a pair of escalators. Sub-surface booking halls built above the tracks are universal but at Rotunda, where the branch and main lines connect, and at Rossio for future interchange, there are two sub-surface halls,

one on either side. The side platforms are 40 m (131 ft) long by
4 m (13 ft) wide, but provision has been made for lengthening to
70 m (230 ft) for four-car trains. At Rossio the platforms are
already 70 m by 8 m (26 ft 3 in) and at Rotunda 70 m long by
6 m (19 ft 8 in) wide. The booking halls are spacious and modern
in appearance with decorative tiling on the walls and good fluorescent lighting. Tickets are issued manually from ticket booths and
exit is by turnstile.

Trains of two cars are run at 2½ minute intervals carrying up to
400 passengers each, giving a line capacity of nearly 10,000 an
hour. It is expected that the interval will ultimately be reduced to
1·5 minutes with 4-car trains, thus increasing the capacity to
30,000 per hour.

The standard 1·435 m (4 ft 8½ in) track gauge is used with
50 kg/m (101 lb/yd) flat-bottomed rails laid in 18 m (59 ft) lengths
and thermit welded. Except in stations where the invert is of concrete, the track is ballasted and has creosoted pine sleepers on
which the rails are secured by elastic spikes upon baseplates. A
conductor rail of 52-kg/m (105 lb/yd) T-section carries the 750-V
d.c. supply, with earth return through the running rails.

Traction current is taken at 10 kV from the national grid via the
Lisbon urban system and is transformed at one substation near
Rotunda station, which has four mercury arc rectifiers of 3,000 kW
total capacity. Local transformers, fed from this substation, by
3000 V cables in the tunnels, provide the 220 V current for signalling and lighting and 380 V for other ancillary services. A diesel
alternator will provide limited power in the event of a failure of the
grid supply.

The signalling is of automatic block type with 50 c/s a.c. track
circuits and colour light signals designed for a maximum of 40
trains an hour, and there are five electric interlocking installations.

Except on a 900-m (½ mile) section near Parque and an area
beneath 18th century buildings in the city centre where extensive
underpinning was necessary, the tunnels were all built by cut and
cover methods. They are generally constructed in mass concrete to
a width of 7·35 m (24 ft 1 in) and height of 4·95 m (16 ft 3 in) for
double track, or 4·50 m (14 ft 9 in) and 4·35 m (14 ft 2 in) for
single track, with an arched roof upon straight sidewalls and a flat
or arched invert. On the deeper section the tunnels were built by

driving a pilot heading about 9 ft square from which the arch section was excavated, shuttered and cast before the main body of the tunnel was excavated and built. The station tunnels are in reinforced concrete with an arched roof span of 9 m (30 ft).

The tunnels are ventilated by fourteen fan installations and are drained by fourteen pumps.

The rolling stock comprises 24 motor cars in service, of German manufacture, and 14 now being built locally. They run in pairs as a two-car unit but can be coupled up to make a four-car train.

The exterior is in red up to the waist rail with grey upper walls and roof. Three double doors on each side give clear openings of 4 ft 6 in. The trains are equipped with fluorescent lighting and a public address system, but there is no forced ventilation.

All four axles are powered by 122 h.p. motors giving sufficient acceleration for an overall speed of $29\frac{1}{2}$ km/hr ($18\frac{1}{2}$ m.p.h.) over a line with stations from 460 to 940 (1510 to 3080 ft) apart, with an average run of 640 m (2010 ft). The cars seat 44 passengers, 16 on lateral seats in the two portions between the doors, and six at each end beyond the doors, and have a total capacity of 200. The overall length is $16\frac{1}{2}$ m (54 ft 2 in), the width is 2·7 m (8 ft $10\frac{1}{2}$ in) and weight $36\frac{1}{2}$ tons.

The cars are maintained in a surface depot near Sete-Rios which is connected to the main line from a point south of the next station, Palhava, by a single-line track, mostly in tunnel, 570 m (1870 ft) long.

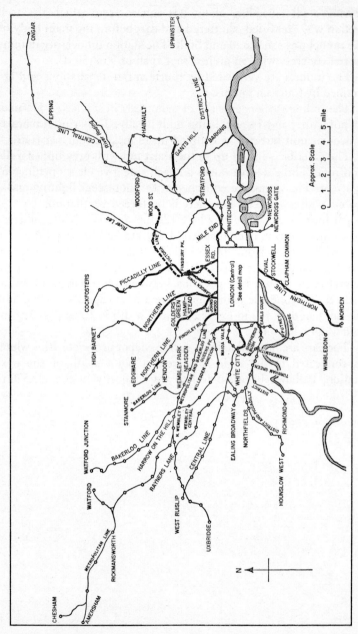

LONDON (General)

London

Since the Romans established a base on the Thames at the nearest point to the sea where it could be forded and the banks were firm enough to unload ships and build roads, London has remained the principal port and focus point of the main roads of Britain. The City of London, on the original Roman site, has less than 5000 people sleeping in it, and the County of London has $3\frac{1}{4}$ million, but the whole Greater London area is populated by over 8 million and London Transport serves $10\frac{1}{4}$ million people, spread over 2000 square miles. A staff of 65,000 men and 11,000 women carried 3153 million passengers in 1962 for an average distance of 2·75 miles each.

The underground railway system was built by a number of rival companies without any thought of co-operation or of easy interchange. To weld the seven lines into a whole has already cost much money, effort and engineering skill, and there is still much to be done. London Transport's trains run over 244 miles of route carrying 668 million passengers (in 1962) for an average journey of 4·57 miles at an overall average speed of 20 m.p.h.

There are two distinct types of line and rolling stock. The subsurface or shallow type includes the Metropolitan of 60 route miles, the District of 45 route miles and the 13 route miles of the Inner Circle, and the rolling stock of these is interchangeable. The tube or deep level lines are the Central with 51 route miles, the Northern of 40 miles, Piccadilly 38, and Bakerloo 32 route miles, and the rolling stock is smaller and interchangeable on all the tubes. The mileages quoted add up to 279 and include 35 miles over which trains of more than one line are operated. The whole system comprises 66 miles of tube tunnel, 22 miles of sub-surface tunnel, and 156 miles of open line.

In the central area trains of up to eight cars are run at 1·5-minute intervals in the rush-hours and 3 minutes in slack periods, serving 273 stations of which 244 are managed by London Transport. These stations, built at various times by different companies,

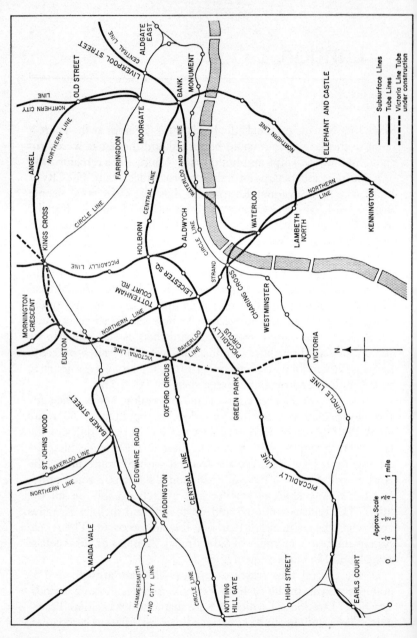

LONDON (Central)

vary considerably in design and decoration. The sub-surface stations nearly all have side platforms about 12 to 14 ft wide with booking halls at or a little below street level, and escalators or lifts are unnecessary. Tube stations generally have side platforms, the few exceptions being on the Northern Line. Some older stations have lifts to surface booking halls, but the modern practice is to have a sub-surface booking hall reached by escalators, or high-speed lifts where the site is not suitable for escalators. The first escalator was installed at Earls Court in 1911 and there were 94 lifts and 188 escalators in service in 1962. At very busy stations there are three parallel escalators, one up, one down, and one reversible according to the traffic flow in peak hours, but the normal provision is one up and one down with a fixed staircase between them. Deeper stations are served by two flights of escalators with intermediate landings and the escalator speed is normally kept at 147 ft per minute, though many can be run faster.

The first proposal for an underground railway in London was made in the eighteen-thirties and in 1851 there was quite serious consideration of a scheme incorporating a road with a width of a hundred feet and tunnel below containing six standard and two wide gauge tracks, between Holborn Hill and King's Cross.

The first sub-surface line was opened from Paddington to Farringdon Street on January 10, 1863, and in the following two years was extended to Hammersmith and Moorgate. The track was equipped with three rails to provide both a 4 ft 8½ in gauge and the Great Western Railway's 7-ft gauge, but in 1869 the broad gauge ceased to be used on this route. This was the birth of the Metropolitan which grew steadily until by 1894 it reached Aldgate in the east and Aylesbury and Chesham in the north.

The District was the second sub-surface line to be opened between High Street Kensington and Westminster in 1868, and was soon extended to Hounslow in the west, Richmond and Putney Bridge in the south, and to Whitechapel in the east. Both these lines were electrified in 1905 and 1906.

The World's first deep-level tube railway, the City and South London, was opened on December 18, 1890, from a point near the Monument in Stockwell, and is still in use as part of the Northern Line. The original intention was to use cable haulage, as was later done in Glasgow, but electric traction was installed before the opening. In 1900 the tube was extended southwards to Clapham Common, and north to the Angel, Islington, and in 1907 it was taken on from Angel to Euston.

In 1898 the only 'outsider' was opened, the London & South Western Railway's tube line of 1½ miles from Waterloo to the Bank. Like the Glasgow line, this never reaches the surface and the trains are maintained in surface sidings at Waterloo to which they are raised by a lift. The line is still owned and operated by British Rail.

The Central Line opened on July 30, 1900, between Shepherd's Bush and the Bank for 5¾ miles beneath the traffic-choked artery of Oxford Street. The fare was twopence for any distance, and the 'twopenny tube' carried 33 million passengers in the first year. The alliterative nickname survived for many years after a sliding scale fare had been introduced in 1909. For the Great Exhibition of 1908 the line was extended westwards to Wood Lane (now White City) and in 1912 the eastern end was taken on to Liverpool Street. It was not until December 1946 that the Central Line was opened to Stratford in the east, though the tunnels had been virtually completed before the Second World War, had been used as public shelters, and had housed a factory for small armament and aircraft components. By 1948 the line was open from West Ruislip to Epping and round a loop via Hainault. From Epping to Ongar was steam-worked until an electrified shuttle service took over in November 1957.

The only tube built with 16 ft diameter tunnels to take main line stock was the Great Northern & City Line, now part of the Northern Line, to take suburban trains into Moorgate from Finsbury Park, a distance of 3½ miles. This was opened on February 14, 1904, with an unusual four-rail system of one conductor rail on each side of the track. It was taken over by the Metropolitan on September 1, 1913, and was converted to tube standards and rolling stock in 1939.

On March 10, 1906, the Bakerloo Line started to run between Baker Street and Waterloo with a depot at Lambeth North. On August 5 it went on to Elephant and Castle, and in the following year to Edgware Road. In 1915 the line had joined up with the London & North Western Railway at Queen's Park and through running to Willesden Junction started in May, to be extended to Watford in 1917. The extension to Stanmore was opened on November 20, 1939.

The Piccadilly Line dates from December 15, 1906, when it ran from Hammersmith to Finsbury Park. The Holborn–Aldwych branch was opened a year later but the remainder of the line between Cockfosters and Northfields was not in service until 1933.

The Hampstead Line (now, with the City & South London, forming the main part of the Northern Line) ran between the Strand and Golders Green from June 22, 1907, and was extended to Charing Cross in 1914. After the First World War, in 1926 the southward extension was completed from Charing Cross to Kennington where it joined the City & South London. The line was then extended to Morden in the south and to Edgware in the north. Between Golders Green and Morden there is continuous tube tunnel for $17\frac{1}{4}$ miles.

Reference has been made to the difficulty and expense of integrating all the separate lines in London, and the evidence of this is most apparent to passengers in the reconstruction of stations to give interchange, but perhaps the greater difficulties arose from different standards of track and tunnels. Changes in these have to be effected unobtrusively and usually without noticeable interference with traffic.

The original City & South London tunnels were of 10 ft 2 in diameter, the first extension was in 10 ft 6 in and the second in 11 ft 6 in diameter iron, and stations were only 200 ft long. In 1922 and 1923 these were enlarged to the standard 11 ft $8\frac{1}{4}$ in on the straight and 12 ft 0 in diameter on curves, to enable the same size rolling stock to be used as on the other tube lines, and the stations were lengthened by a hundred and fifty feet.

The Central Line tube was 11 ft $8\frac{1}{4}$ in diameter but not built to modern standards of accuracy and ten thousand rings of iron were enlarged by rebuilding with packings in 1938 and 1939. At times the work was in progress at more than thirty points and simultaneously the track was being relaid from bridge rail, on longitudinal timbers, to the standard of bullhead rail on sleepers, stations were being lengthened and the approaches regraded, and the original central third rail system was being changed to the standard fourth rail system. The final change over was effected in one week-end, as was the conversion of the Great Northern & City Line.

The sub-surface lines in London were practically all built by cut and cover beneath the main streets. The tube lines have all been built, so far as possible, in the London clay which is ideal for shield driving. However, even at the deepest points such as Hampstead, 192 ft below the street, it is necessary for lift shafts or escalators to penetrate the more difficult ground, and where the tubes are relatively shallow, as under the marshes of the Lea Valley at the eastern end of the Central Line tubes, it has been necessary to use air at considerable pressure.

The usual London tube is of cast iron segments bolted together into a ring which is built up within an extension of the actual shield. As the shield moves forward a space of about an inch is left between the cast iron and the clay and this is filled by pumping in cement and sand grout. Similar construction using reinforced concrete segments was used for part of the last Central Line extension.

For the Victoria Line, now being built, the lining of concrete or iron is not bolted but made up with a hinged joint. After erection the lining is expanded against the clay, by jacks inserted in certain joints for the iron, or by tapered keys driven into the concrete rings. The Victoria Line tunnels will have an interior diameter of 12 ft 8 in and will run from Victoria across the busiest areas of London for eleven miles to the north-east, connecting Victoria, Euston and King's Cross main line termini and giving frequent interchange with the other underground lines.

On the open sections and in the sub-surface tunnels the track is ballasted with softwood creosoted sleepers and 95-lb/yd bullhead rail secured in chairs by steel or wooden keys. Numerous short sections of flat-bottomed track with a variety of fastenings have been installed for test. In the tubes the sleepers are jarrah, an Australian hardwood, and are embedded in a concrete foundation. The gauge throughout is nominally 4 ft 8½ in. The running rails, delivered in 60-ft lengths, are welded into a maximum length of 300 ft which is dictated by the available length of space in the depot at Fulham, where a flash-butt welding machine is installed.

The conductor rails are two, a negative nominally at 220 V below neutral in the centre and a positive nominally 440 V above neutral at the side of the track. The negative rail is always held by porcelain insulators on the centre of the sleepers while insulators for the positive are upon the ends of the sleepers of the ballasted track, and on special wooden blocks sunk in the concrete of tube tracks. These rails are welded into lengths of up to half a mile. The traction current is collected by top contact and supplied from substations connected by 33 kW cables to the three power stations, Lots Road, Greenwich and Neasden, owned by London Transport.

Where necessary in the open sections protection is given against the formation of ice upon the conductor rails, by small tanks of de-icing fluid inset in the rail and having a roller partly immersed and standing slightly above the rail so that the fluid is carried and spread on the rail by the shoes of the trains. During non-traffic hours long lengths of conductor rail are also heated by short-circuiting the traction current.

All the points necessary to operate the service are kept free of ice and snow by electrical heaters. These are installed in a tank full of oil at the side of the track and are automatically switched on when the temperature falls near to freezing point. Oil at a thermostatically controlled heat is pumped through pipes to the vital part of the point operating mechanism and passes through holes in the chairs beneath the stock rails and switches to keep them warm enough to operate freely in the worst of weather.

The collection and checking of tickets employs a large number of staff and it is virtually impossible for them to verify that each ticket is being correctly used. Experiments are in progress towards a complete system of automatic ticket checking. At Turnham Green on the District Line, tickets are obtained from a machine which stamps a code upon them in magnetic ink, to indicate the station of origin, the fare paid, the date and, when necessary, the time of issue. At three other stations different types of automatic barriers are being tested in conjunction with a machine which checks all the details coded on the ticket. The passenger must insert his ticket in the machine which will accept it and release the barrier if it is correct in every particular or will reject it and keep the barrier closed if there is any discrepancy. The tests are going on at lightly used stations but the ultimate aim is to extend the system to cover even the busiest stations on the system.

Signalling is automatic with two aspect colour lights and train-stops, all running lines being continuously track circuited with sections varying from a hundred feet to a mile in length. Normally de-energized track circuits 11 ft 6 in long are used to detect that trains have stopped, mainly for clearing warning and calling on signals. Repeating signals with green and yellow aspects are extensively used and additional fog repeating signals are installed in the open. The lines are signalled generally for 40 trains an hour, and in areas where speed control signalling is installed, the signalling can cope with 48 trains an hour.

At junctions route control systems are widely used, routes being pre-selected by miniature levers which allow for a second, possibly conflicting, route to be prepared before the first has cleared. Many signal cabins are remotely controlled, the lever being operated by air cylinders actuated by electromagnets controlled from levers or push buttons in a central cabin. In emergency all cabins can be manually operated.

London Transport has carried the automation of signalling forward to the point where a whole day's service over complicated junctions is operated by a programme machine which can work alone, so long as not more than a few trains are running in an incorrect sequence. It is only when there is something seriously wrong with the service that a supervisor in a central control office has to advise the machine what to do or make it act on his instructions. If trains arrive at a junction in the wrong sequence according to the day's programme, the machine remembers this and makes the necessary adjustment to the service and it checks that each train has been described on the platform indicators for the route that it is to follow. If in trouble it warns the supervisor who can direct the action of the machine, even making it deal with an extra train not shown in the programme. Such machines are already in use for all the more important junctions.

The first automatically driven train carrying passengers in London ran in April 1963. Early in 1964 the complete service between Woodford and Hainault, a distance of 4 miles, was automatically driven. The installation differs from the general pattern in providing for safety signalling instructions to be given to the train by a system independent of that which gives routine driving instructions.

Safety is ensured by coded track circuits fed with 125 c/s a.c. supply in pulses of four frequencies which are picked up from the running rails by induction coils mounted in front of the train. The code for free running at maximum speed is 420 pulses a minute. A code of 270 allows running at 22 m.p.h. and gives an emergency brake application if 25 m.p.h. is exceeded; it is also used to re-start a train after stopping at a signal. The 180 code shuts off the motors and, again, causes emergency braking if the speed is over 25 m.p.h. Finally, 120 pulses per minute causes an emergency brake application under all conditions and the absence of any code has the same effect.

As each train passes over any track circuit it leaves behind it a section coded at 120 for a distance sufficient to halt a following train without risk of collision.

Routine driving instructions are given through a separate pair of coils on the train which pick up higher frequency signals injected into the running rails and effective over a 'spot' only 10 ft long.

These signals may cause three degrees of braking. On all the trains of London Transport a 'retardation controller' is used to give a fixed rate of deceleration, independent of the gradient or loading of the train. This consists of a column of mercury in a curved glass tube. The inertia of the mercury causes it to swing back from its normal, at rest or steady speed, position through a distance proportional to the deceleration of the train, and when it is in the correct position it makes electrical contact to complete a circuit which holds the brakes on. If the mercury swings too far the brake is released until it returns to the desired position. On the automatic train three such retardation controllers are used, set for slight, normal, and full braking.

Each 'spot' is energized for 127 cycles of the frequency of the current injected, is then dead for 127 cycles and alternately alive and dead for 127 cycles. A generator on an axle of the train generates a frequency proportional to the speed, 100 c/s corresponding to each 1 m.p.h.

Apparatus on the train counts the number of cycles generated on the train during the time the 'spot' is energized—that is for 127 cycles of the injected current. If the number is greater than 127 the brakes are fully applied; if it is less a light application is made.

As a train approaches a station it passes over a number of spots. The first may be 4500 c/s, allowing a speed up to 45 m.p.h. and the next 4000 c/s (40 m.p.h.) and so on down to 1000 c/s (10 m.p.h.). Finally at 4 m.p.h. the brakes are eased off to give a gentle stop.

Two higher frequencies are also used: 20 kc (representing 200 m.p.h.) which causes a normal brake application to persist until a train stops at a signal, and 150 kc which only switches off the motors causing the train to coast freely.

The rolling stock fleet consists of 2758 tube cars and 1464 sub-surface cars. The latest of each type is recognizable by the unpainted aluminium exterior finish which, incidentally, saves over a ton of the red paint previously used for every seven cars. Both types are rubber sprung with vertical and lateral hydraulic shock absorbers.

The interior of the new tube stock is finished in maroon and grey, and the cars seat 40 in a motor and 42 in a trailer on a combination of longitudinal and transverse seats, with a crush capacity of 162 or 178 passengers. Two double doors on each side of all cars give 4 ft 6 in clear opening and additional single doors at the ends of trailers open to 2 ft 3 in. These air-operated doors are top hung, without the bottom tracks which were liable to be jammed by grit or other objects.

The cars are 52 ft 3 in and 51 ft 3 in long overall, 8 ft 6 in wide and 9 ft 5½ in high. They are in units of one trailer and two motors, or of four cars by the addition of a motor without a driving compartment. All control gear is mounted below the floor in a detachable case and is of the well-proven electro-pneumatic camshaft type. Each motor has two 80-h.p. nose-suspended motors driving 31 in diameter wheels through helical gears. An electro-pneumatic braking system with retardation control operates two non-metallic blocks on every wheel giving service braking at 2·25 m.p.h./s. Emergency braking of 3 m.p.h./s is by air brakes.

Each tube train driver is equipped with a portable telephone set and through every tube a pair of bare wires run along the tunnel walls. In emergency the driver leans out of his cab and pinches these together. The resulting short circuit sounds an alarm in the substation and cuts off the traction current. Then the driver connects a portable telephone and can speak to the substation attendant or controller. There is also a telephone permanently mounted in the cab and if he connects this to the same tunnel wires the driver can by-pass the substation and speak directly to the controller by radio frequency carrier waves in those wires. True radio communication is not practicable within the iron tubes, but it is used for communicating with the breakdown services, on the surface, in any emergency.

The new sub-surface stock have transverse seats for 58 in the trailers and 54 in the motors, with 4 tip-up seats and a crush capacity of 172 and 189 passengers. The interior is finished in grey and maroon with an extensive use of laminated plastics. The two pairs of double doors on either side of the driving motors, and three in the trailers, each give a clear opening of 4 ft 6 in and are operated by the guard. The cars are 53 ft 0½ in overall, 9 ft 8 in wide and 12 ft 1 in from rail level to roof, weighing 31 tons for a motor and 21 tons for a trailer car. They run in units of motor, two trailers, motor, to couple into four- or eight-car trains.

Each axle of the motor cars has a nose-suspended 60 h.p. motor driving 36 in wheels through helical gears. Braking is electro-pneumatic with retardation control operating two non-metallic blocks on each wheel, giving a service retardation of 2·25 m.p.h. per second and in emergency 3 m.p.h. per second.

A wide range of performance is required because in the central area the stations average only half a mile apart and loadings may be heavy, while in the country the distance may be up to 13 miles between stations with light loading. Therefore the driver has control of the setting of the acceleration relay notches as well as the field strength. The designed maximum speed with 60 per cent full field is 60 m.p.h.

The rolling stock due to be delivered in 1967 for the new Victoria Line is designed for fully automatic driving. The driver must press two separate buttons to start the train (a single button might be pressed accidentally) and while operating automatically an illuminated panel will indicate to him what safety code signal or driving command is being received. He can take over manual control of the train, but then the speed is to be limited to 25 m.p.h. in the signalled sections and to 10 m.p.h. in unsignalled sidings and depots or if the signalling is out of use. If these speeds are exceeded an audible warning will sound and the brakes will be applied automatically.

95

The fleet will consist of 240 cars to form 27 trains each in two units of motor, two trailers, motor, with 26 space cars. In the event of trouble on one unit the driver will be able to isolate the motors and drive on the other unit only. Braking will be rheostatic down to a low speed at which conventional brake blocks take over. In addition to the normal communications the driver will have a public address system to all cars.

These aluminium cars will be recognizable by the streamlined appearance of the curved front and windscreen, the absence of side doors to the driver's cab, the twin headlamps set flush in the front panels and the larger windows, double glazed against noise. Ventilation is by external slots above the windows leading to ducts behind the advertisement panels which will act as control flaps. The seating in motor cars will be the same as in existing stock, but to provide more standing room all seating in the trailers will be longitudinal.

Almost certainly the first attempts at constructing a tube railway were made in London in 1861 when an experimental line two-thirds of a mile long was built in Battersea Park. Within a tube of 2 ft 6 in diameter a carrier ran upon rails. This was fitted with a diaphragm, probably of leather, which fitted the interior of the tube and a vacuum was formed in front of it by means of a fan, so that atmospheric pressure drove the carrier along. The success of this experiment led to a line being built to carry mail from Euston to the North Western District Post Office. This opened with success in February 1863 and was followed by a larger tube of 4 ft 6 in diameter from Euston to the General Post Office at St. Martin's le Grand in November 1865. The results were discouraging and it was not until December 1927 that the present Post Office Tube was opened.

This is a line of 6·44 miles of 2 ft gauge with 8 stations. The running tunnel is a single 9 ft diameter tube containing two tracks. At stations there are two separate 7 ft tubes containing a platform, a stopping line and a through line. The more important stations have a reversing loop at one or both ends and some have room for a third track. Stations are from 90 ft long at the West Parcel Office to 313 ft at the main sorting office of Mount Pleasant, where also there is a maintenance depot. The maximum depth is 90 ft and the average of 70 ft below street level.

Traction is by 440-V d.c. in a third rail and automatic driving is attained by brakes that are held off by the traction current and applied when that is cut off. A train in any one section of track automatically cuts off the current from the section behind it. Trains are slowed to enter a station by a section on which the power is reduced to 150 V, and are stopped by the brakes being applied by a section with current cut off. Points and dead sections at stations are controlled from small lever frames.

Trains run at a maximum speed of 35 m.p.h. and a minimum headway of two minutes. They are of one or two cars, each car carrying four containers of mail and powered by a 22-h.p. motor on each of the two bogies. There are 50 cars and three battery cars for emergency use.

As late as 1958 a short extension was built to Rathbone Place when the Western District Office was moved there.

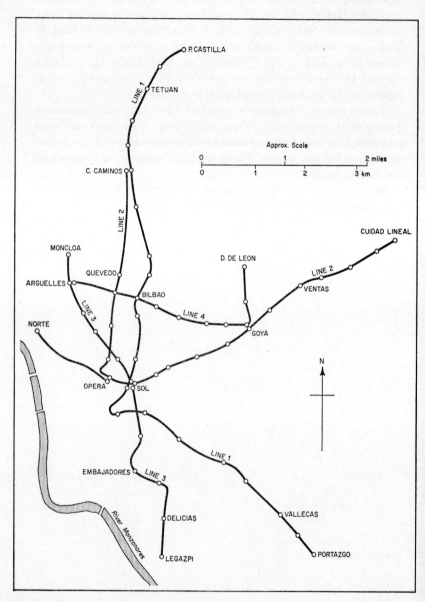

P. CASTILLA

LINE 1

TETUAN

C. CAMINOS

LINE 2

Approx. Scale

0   1   2 miles
0   1   2   3 km

CUIDAD LINEAL

MONCLOA

D. DE LEON

QUEVEDO

LINE 2

VENTAS

ARGUELLES

BILBAO

LINE 3

LINE 4

NORTE

GOYA

N

OPERA

SOL

LINE 1

EMBAJADORES

LINE 3

VALLECAS

DELICIAS

LEGAZPI

River Manzanares

PORTAZGO

MADRID

Madrid

The Puerta del Sol is the traditional centre of Madrid and around it are the official buildings, large offices and areas of dense population, served by narrow twisting streets which become wide and straight as they reach the newer parts of the city and the outlying suburbs. In the first twenty years of this century the streets became choked with cars and carts drawn by animals, and the many tramcars formed almost continuous slow processions.

In 1917 a group of engineers obtained a concession from the Government and formed the Compania Metropolitano de Madrid and started construction of the section from Puerta del Sol to Cuatro Caminos, 3·6 km long (2¼ miles) which they opened on October 17, 1919. This line was constructed by contractors but in view of its immediate success, the company formed its own organization to construct further works.

By 1925 Line 1 had reached Vallecas in the south-east and Line 2 extended to Ventas in the east, Quevedo in the north and Norte in the west, adding 11·2 km (7 miles) to the system. Line 1 was carried on to Tetuan from Cuatro Caminos and Line 2 from Quevedo to Cuatro Caminos in 1929, with a branch from Goya to Diego de Leon in 1932. In the last days before the civil war started on July 18, 1936, the first section of Line 3 was completed from Puerta del Sol to Embajadores and was opened on August 8, making the total length of the system 20·6 km (13 miles).

After the Civil War Line 3 was extended from Puerta del Sol to Arguelles in 1941, Line 4 was opened between Arguelles and Goya in 1944, Line 3 extended from Embajadores to Delicias in 1949, and on to Legazpi in 1951.

The last group of extensions, which brought the total route length of the system to 33⅓ km (nearly 21 miles), were of Line 1 from Tetuan to Plaza Castilla (1 km) in 1961 and from Vallecas to Portazgo (1 km) in 1962, Line 3 from Arguelles to Moncloa

($\frac{5}{8}$ km) in 1963 and Line 2 from Ventas to Cuidad Lineal ($2\frac{1}{2}$ km) on May 28, 1964.

The system now comprises $33\frac{1}{3}$ km (21 m) of route with 58 stations, and carries nearly 456 million passengers a year. There is a flat rate fare of one peseta and a transfer ticket to the Suburban railway, which also has a flat fare of one peseta, costs $1\frac{1}{2}$ pesetas. This, a state-owned suburban railway runs from Plaza Espana for about $9\frac{1}{2}$ km (6 miles) to Carabanchel in the south-west, serving 6 stations and about 18 million passengers a year.

The density of traffic on the Metro, judged by a comparison of the total annual number of passengers compared with the route length, is extremely high, nearly 15 million passengers for every kilometre of route. No doubt this is due to the easy access to the shallow stations and their close spacing, on the average only 550 m or 600 yds apart. There are virtually no peak hours, the volume of traffic being almost constant from 7.30 a.m. to 9.30 p.m.

The length of a train is limited to four cars by the length of the platform, but starting with Line 1 these are now being lengthened from 60 to 90 m (195 to 295 ft) to allow for six-car trains. The normal design of station has two side platforms $4\frac{1}{4}$ m (13 ft 11 in) wide, but at some terminal stations there is an unusual arrangement of one side platform and one island, with one track between them used to receive passenger trains, and the outer track used as a siding.

Sub-surface booking halls are the standard, and with the shallow construction, escalators are seldom necessary. However, at Puerto del Sol Line 1 passes over Lines 2 and 3, which are at a depth of 15 m to avoid underground services, and escalators are provided. These are installed in an unusual but very pleasing shaft with a ribbed arch roof and ample fluorescent lighting. Each line has a separate Sol station, but all three are connected by wide passages and are easily reached from seven entrances on the pavements around the square.

The station platforms are surfaced with hexagonal tiles under a flat arched roof, lit by fluorescent tubes, with glazed tile walls upon which large standard sized commercial advertisements are mounted in frames.

The subsoil of Madrid consists of strata of clay and sand in which construction is relatively easy, and the two million in-

habitants are massed on the north-east side of the River Manzanares which the Metro has not yet crossed. Cut and cover
methods have generally been employed to build horseshoe shaped
single tunnels 6·86 m (22 ft 6 in) wide by 5·36 m) (17 ft 7 in) high
on the straight, and 7·18 m (24 ft 7 in) by 5·55 m (18 ft 2 in) on
sharp curves, i.e. less than 90 m (about 300 ft) radius. Where there
was only very shallow cover the tunnels are of box shape with a
flat arch roof in concrete, or with a jack arch roof supported by
cross girders at 27-in centres carried on concrete side walls and a
central support of a steel joist embedded in concrete. In this construction the clear way for each track is 3·35 m (10 ft 11 in), with
14 in allowed for the central support.

Ventilation is provided by openings corbelled out from near the
centre of the tunnel roof to the side of the roadway, in order to
avoid the usual double tram track in the centre of the road, and
covered with a cast steel grating.

The track gauge is 1·445 m (4 ft 8⅞ in) and the flat-bottomed
rails weigh 45 kg/m (91 lb/yd) in 18-m (59 ft) lengths, with fully
staggered joints and fastened by baseplates and clips upon oak or
creosoted beech sleepers. The track is ballasted except for some
sharp curves and in the station grounds, where timber blocks are
embedded in a concrete invert.

Signalling employs a.c. track circuits, generally extending from
the exit of one station to the exit of the next, so that a train cannot
leave one station until the next station has been cleared. Most of
the stations are less than 800 metres apart, but where the distance
is greater, an intermediate track circuit and signal is installed. The
colour light signals are operated by 220-V current locally transformed at each location from a 1,000-V a.c. feed cable. At Puerta
del Sol, Cuatro Caminos and Goya there is automatic electric
interlocking with push button control.

The traction current is taken from an overhead grooved copper
wire suspended by insulators from cross wires at every 60 ft and
fed in sections averaging 1 km in length. Each section is connected
to the next by a switch which closes when there is a potential
difference greater than 50 Volts between them.

The high-tension supply from the Hydroelectric Companies
grid system is stepped down from three-phase 15 kV to 600 V d.c.
at four substations, Quevedo 8000 kW, Salamanca 7000 kW,

Pacifico 5000 kW, and Delicias 1600 kW. The Quevedo substation lies between Lines 1 and 2, feeding both, and that at Salamanca is between Lines 2 and 4, about ½ km west of Goya and also feeding both lines.

The fleet of rolling stock comprises 224 motors and 146 trailers, which run in motor and trailer units permanently coupled. Each motor car has every axle powered by a 100-h.p. motor with an electro-pneumatic control system. Braking is by compressed air but rheostatic braking is being tested and, in view of the existence of continuous gradients of 1 in 20, electromagnetic brakes are also being considered.

The cars are entirely of steel with the two walls forming part of the load bearing structure. They are 14·3 m (46 ft 11 in) long and 2·4 m (7 ft 10½ in) wide with four doors on each side controlled by the guard. Seating is provided for 36 passengers in single back-to-back lateral seats on either side of a wide central gangway.

There is no pantograph but current is collected by a light trolley apparatus of trolleybus type. The cars and all equipment are entirely of Spanish make.

Rolling stock maintenance is mainly concentrated at Cuatro Caminos on Lines 1 and 2, but there is a small depot at Ventas and an underground depot at Arguelles.

The forward planning of the Metro Company when first formed has one unique feature, in that an affiliated company was established, while the first section of the line was still being built, to purchase land around Cuatro Caminos and develop it with all main services into housing estates, a park, and a stadium. All of great benefit to the community and, incidentally, to the Metro.

Milan

The centre of Milan is the world-famous cathedral surrounded by a maze of narrow streets which are almost equally famed for traffic congestion. It is said to be impossible for a stranger to visit the Cathedral by car for, if lucky enough to find it, he will be unable to park his vehicle anywhere less than a mile away and must again face the problem of finding the way on foot. The old city houses half a million people and the surrounding areas of industrial and housing development account for another million.

The tramway system is extremely elaborate, efficient and obstructive to other surface traffic. It is hoped to eliminate the trams from the narrow streets and to reduce the tidal wave of commuters cars by constructing the world's most modern and best integrated underground railway system, and the portion already in service bristles with points of interest.

As early as 1905 proposals were formulated but not until 1955 did the Ministry of Transport sanction construction. The tunnelling for the first line was virtually completed in 1961 by a company controlled by the municipality and then it was decided that the equipment and operation should be the responsibility of the Azienda Tranviaria Municipale (ATM) who already controlled all bus, trolleybus, tram and suburban railway lines. The system already planned will consist of four through lines interlaced beneath the city having a total length of $36\frac{1}{2}$ km ($22\frac{3}{4}$ miles) with provision made for future extension at both ends of each line. The lines are to be known by colours, Red No. 1, Green No. 2, Yellow No. 3 and Blue No. 4 and will be distinguished by the predominance of the nominated colour in the decoration of the stations. The plan is for them to be built in that sequence.

The construction of Line 1, the Red Line, was approved in September 1958 and it was opened on November 1, 1964, over $12\frac{1}{2}$ km ($7\frac{3}{4}$ miles) from Marelli in the north to the Cathedral, where it turns west to Lotto in the Hippodrome area in the north-west.

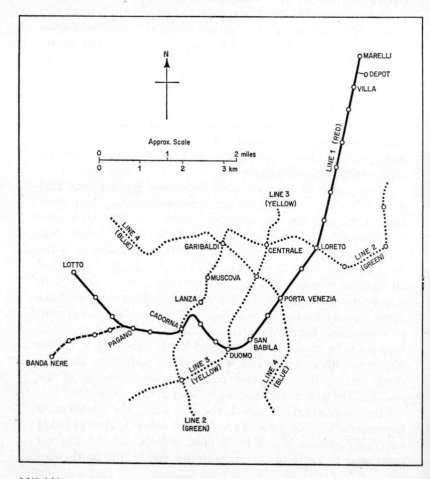

MILAN

From Pagano there is a 2-km (1¼ mile) branch to Banda Nere which is still under construction.

Six-car trains are run at 1·5 minute intervals in the peak periods, giving a capacity of over 50,000 passengers an hour, and running at an overall speed of 30 km/hr (19 m.p.h.) There are 21 stations of which four have been designed as interchange points for the future lines, and the Banda Nere branch will have four more. This means close spacing of stations at an average distance of ⅓ mile and a minimum of ¼ mile. Side platforms are used, 116 m (380 ft) long and sub-surface booking halls are reached by escalators, but at shallow stations these only serve ascending passengers at present. The exit stairs are generally twice as wide as the downwards, entering, stairways. Many of the platforms are not much more than 12 ft wide in contrast to the very spacious design of the booking halls and other passenger accommodation.

The decoration of the stations is effective and economical with a distinctive style which is soothing rather than striking. The walls are finished with metal sheets faced in a mottled plastic and set out from the concrete to give room behind for pipes and other services and to allow commercial showcases and advertisements to be set flush with them and to be lighted from within. The false wall finishes some distance below the ceiling which, with the upper part of the walls, is of a rough texture in subdued colours. Lighting is by fluorescent tubes behind translucent plastic shades and is noticeably free from glare. The whole effect is in sharp contrast to the ultra-modern, flashy effect of renovated stations on some other systems, and appears to have been achieved without extravagant expenditure on the more permanent decorative materials such as marble, ceramic tiles or glass mosaic.

Particular attention has been given to the reduction of manpower, and in addition to having only one man on the train, one man controls each station entrance. Turnstiles with three arms guard the entrances and the tickets are checked by a machine which detects that they carry a metal varnish on the end and, by removing this, ensures that they cannot be re-used. Season ticket and pass holders use a separate passage under the scrutiny of the one man staff. Exit is through a barrier, opening in one direction only and operated by the weight of the passenger as he approaches.

The station traffic is controlled by a very complete system of closed-circuit television. Each platform is scanned by a camera which has both a long and short focus lens, and these are controlled from a monitor set in each of the offices occupied by the man in charge of the station entrances. In addition screens are available to the stationmaster, and the central traffic controller at San Babila can connect his screen to any of the platform cameras. Provision has also been made for a screen in the central control office to scan all the stations in turn by an automatic time switch. The television works on 625 lines.

The central traffic controller at San Babila is in telephonic communication with all booking halls and can speak over the public address system of any one, or all, stations by pressing an appropriate button. He can transmit teleprinter messages to any one, or all, of nine stations, and from any of these stations teleprinter messages can be sent back to the controller, to any other station or to five other stations simultaneously.

The station clocks are automatically corrected by a master clock at San Babila which, in turn, is controlled from a radio transmitter at the Astronomical Observatory. This relays impulses at set intervals which are received and decoded at San Babila. Each clock has also a mechanical movement that is kept wound to ensure 18 hours' operation in the event of a power failure.

The emergency telephone system for train drivers consists of a portable telephone set with magnetic plugs that can be inserted into jacks installed in the tunnel at 50-m (164 ft) intervals to give connections to the central control. By the side of each jack there is a push button which cuts off the traction current.

The signalling is arranged for 40 trains an hour and has been designed with a view to full automation of train driving at a later date. In the driver's cab there is a four-colour light indicator operated by induction from electrical impulses in the running rails. Each track circuit can be energized by 75 c/s a.c.; 270 impulses a minute gives a green aspect and permits speeds up to 85 km/hr (53 m.p.h.); 120 gives yellow and 50 km/hr (31 m.p.h.); 50 impulses gives purple and 15 km/hr ($9\frac{1}{2}$ m.p.h.). No impulses, or continuous alternating current, operates the red aspect and the brakes. The usual provision is made for automatic brake application if the driver does not react to the signal.

Fixed lineside signals are also installed because the drivers are mainly recruited from the tramway service and will have to become accustomed to cab signalling. At present the fixed signals are regarded of primary importance and the cab signals as continuous repeaters.

Signals and points can be locally controlled from seven signal cabins or centrally from San Babila when the traffic controller has an illuminated diagram displaying the state of all points and track circuits.

The track is of 1·435-m (4 ft 8½ in) gauge, and in the 12·321 km now open there are 36 curves, of which 11 have a radius of less than 200 m (656 ft). The rails are 50 kg/m (101 lb/yd) flat-bottomed throughout, welded continuously and for nearly the whole distance laid in the conventional fashion upon wooden sleepers and ballast. However, the question of track design has been closely studied and some interesting experiments have resulted, particularly over 2 km of single track between Cadorna and Pagano. Over this section the reduction of vibration has been the paramount consideration because of the proximity of the Cathedral and other important historic buildings. Before installing this new type of track an experimental length of 200 metres was fully tested, in the open, on the Adda express line.

The new construction starts from a level invert of lean concrete upon which neoprene strips 20 mm × 20 mm (0·75 × 0·75 in) are laid across at ½ m (20 in) intervals and between them the space is filled with slabs of a non-elastic foam urea plastic. This is covered with waterproof sheets of polythene and a slab of reinforced concrete is cast upon it, 20 cm (8 in) thick and 2½ m (8 ft 2½ in) wide for each track, in 12-m (39 ft 4 in) lengths with an expansion joint between each. The baseplates are levelled on a bed of epoxy resin and quartz sand and secured by two bolts inserted into holes drilled in the concrete and filled with epoxy. The rails are secured upon rubber pads 11 mm (0·43 in) thick by two C-shaped spring steel clips.

The section on which this track is laid includes a curve of 137 m (450 ft) radius, a reverse curve of 170 m (558 ft) radius and a connection between the two tracks. Tests have shown that the vibration transmitted to the ground is only one-third as strong as on ballasted track, but the cost is some 70 per cent greater and the track is slightly more noisy. An extended test over 6 km (3¾ miles) of the Addia line is also in hand.

Another 200 m (656 ft) of single track has been built in the same way but without the Neoprene insulation, and the noise and vibration over this section are considerably greater. Also 1 km of double track has been laid on timber sleepers and ballast using the same rubber pads and fastenings as on the concrete track.

A fourth rail system has been adopted to avoid the possibility of electrolytic corrosion of the many pipes buried in the damp sub-soil of the city. The central negative rail is of the conventional flat-bottomed section 52 kg/m (105 lb/yd), welded into lengths of 100 m (328 ft) with expansion joints between each. The positive, outside rail is of T-section, arranged for side contact and carried by glass fibre insulators on brackets at 4 m (13 ft 2 in) apart. It is protected throughout by a strip of laminated plastic shaped to cover the top and back of the rail. The conductivity of the negative rail is increased by an aluminium bar bolted to both sides of the web and the positive rail has a similar bar bolted to the upper side of the horizontal portion.

The 750 V d.c. traction current is taken from seven sub-stations, spaced about 2 km apart, fed from the city supply at 23 kV and having a total capacity of 24·750 kW. These are all remotely controlled from San Babila where the Central Electrification control office has been designed to accommodate all the re-mote control apparatus for the ultimate system of four lines. Two more substations will come into use with the Pagano to Banda Nere branch.

The running tunnels are reinforced concrete box sections 7½ m (24 ft 7 in) wide by 3·9 m (12 ft 9 in) from rail level to the lowest point of the straight ribs, 3 ft deep by 1 ft thick at 5 ft centres, which support an almost flat membrane a foot thick. Rail level is never less than 8¾ m (28 ft 8 in) below street level, to avoid the services under the roads and to leave room for reasonably high booking halls.

The city is built upon sand and gravel mixed with large flat water-worn pebbles and boulders and with a high ground water level. This soil does not require heavy timbering during excava-tion but is fairly stable. The ingenious Milan method of excava-tion was therefore developed from a technique used extensively in drilling for oil, also known as the Bentonite or I.C.O.S. process.

The Milan process of cut and cover construction was developed on a first experimental section of Line 1. The process consists of digging narrow trenches along the line of the side walls of the tunnel to a depth of a few feet and lightly concreting the two faces to support them. Then they are filled with a slurry of a particular volcanic clay akin to fullers' earth and known as bentonite. This mixture is like a jelly when undisturbed but becomes liquid when it is stirred up.

A narrow grab is used to deepen the trench and as work goes on more bentonite is poured in until the full depth of the side walls has been reached. The bentonite penetrates an inch or two into the soil and sets firmly enough to stick together the particles of sand and stone so that, so long as the trench is full of bentonite, the walls will not collapse. When a length of bentonite-filled trench is ready, a section of prefabricated steel reinforcement is lowered to the correct position. Concrete is pumped in through a pipe at the bottom of the trench and displaces the bentonite upwards to flow into the next section of trench being excavated.

By this process the tunnel side walls are finished without completely closing the street above, and without the expense of timbering or the danger to men working in a deep narrow trench. It is then necessary to close the street for a short time while the tunnel roof is built in a shallow excavation, but soon it can be reinstated while the bulk of the tunnel is being dug out below.

Close to the foundations of old buildings the sections of trench are made very short and the next section is not excavated until the concrete of the first has set. In effect the wall is built as a line of piles without noise, vibration or danger of settlement.

Before the type of rolling stock was decided upon tests were made with pneumatic-tyred vehicles, of types similar to those used in Paris, in conjunction with the great firms of Lancia, Fiat, Italian General Electric and Pirelli. The final decision was in favour of steel-tyred wheels with rubber inserts between the rim and hub with steel coils enclosed in rubber for both primary and secondary springing.

The cars are all motored, permanently coupled in pairs, with a driving cab at each end. The first 60 cars carried 26 on longitudinal seats with 187 standing but a second order for 24 cars specifies lateral seats for 32 and room for 174 standing. The bodies are aluminium on steel underframes finished inside with plastic panelling over a layer of sound-insulating material and the floors are of wood laid upon cork insulation and covered with grooved rubber sheets. Four pairs of doors on each side are pneumatically operated by the driver. Ventilation is natural, by external roof fittings; lighting is fluorescent, giving 28 foot-candles at reading level and filament lamps are used for emergency lighting.

These motor cars are 17·54 m (57 ft 6 in) long overall, 2·85 m (9 ft 3 in) wide, 3·5 m (11 ft 6 in) from rail level and weigh 32 tons. The bogies each carry two 120 h.p. motors mounted longitudinally and driving 0·82-m (32¼ in) diameter wheels through a Cardan shaft and bevel gear final drive. Braking is by a self-balancing combination of rheostatic and compressed air systems with the air brakes acting upon discs keyed to the axle. A service rate of deceleration up to 5½ km/h (3½ m.p.h.) per second is achieved. The emergency brake is of the 'tramway' magnetic shoe type acting upon the rails and when it is operated sand is automatically applied to give a deceleration up to 7·2 km/h (4½ m.p.h.) per second. The acceleration rate is unusually high at 5·4 km/h (3⅜ m.p.h.) per second for starting. This is rather high for passenger comfort but is provided in order to include a trailer in the train at a later date. The maximum speed is 80 km/h (50 m.p.h.) which, with the high acceleration and rate of braking is ample to give an overall speed of 30 km/h (19 m.p.h.) over a line with stations averaging 600 m (653 yards) apart and a maximum spacing of 750 m (820 yards).

In the depot, between Villa and Marelli where the stock is maintained, it has been thought safer not to use conductor rails but to allow the cars to enter on an overhead system, with running rail return and a small pantograph on the car roof.

Montreal

Montreal started in 1610 as a fur trading post and in 1940, when the first proposals were made for an underground system, there were half a million inhabitants and serious traffic congestion. Until 1961, when the population had grown to nearly 2 million, all proposals were rejected. On May 23, 1962, a start was made on a system of three lines 21½ miles long and mainly in tunnel.

The city looks southwards across the St. Lawrence river and the Ile St. Helene and the long narrow Ile Notre Dame, which separates the river from the St. Lawrence Seaway. It is on these two islands that the World Fair of 1967 is to be held, and because of this an extra line No. 4 is being constructed while Line 3 is in abeyance. Line 3 was to have run parallel to Line 2 from north to south using the Canadian National main tracks and tunnel under the 700-ft Mount Royal, but is now being reconsidered.

Line 1, from Atwater to Frontenac, runs east to west through the City centre for 4·33 miles. By January 1965 3½ miles of tunnel had been blasted through rock and over 2 miles had been lined with concrete. Line 2 runs from Henri Bourassa in the north to cross Line 1 at Berri-de-Montigny and then turns west to Bonaventure, a total distance of 8·22 miles of which nearly 7 miles had been tunnelled and over 15¼ miles concreted up to January 1965. Line 4 runs for 3·01 miles westwards from Berri-de-Montigny under the St. Lawrence river at a depth of 40 ft below the bed to a station on Ile St. Helene and on again beneath the south branch of the river, Ile Notre Dame and the St. Lawrence Seaway to Rive Sud station on the south bank. In January 1965 two thirds of the whole 15½-mile system had been tunnelled and more than half had been lined with concrete.

Montreal is built in a hilly district where the underlying grey limestone rock often breaks the surface and 11 of the 15½ miles is being tunnelled through the rock with explosives. In order to obtain quick results no less than 19 separate tunnelling contracts were

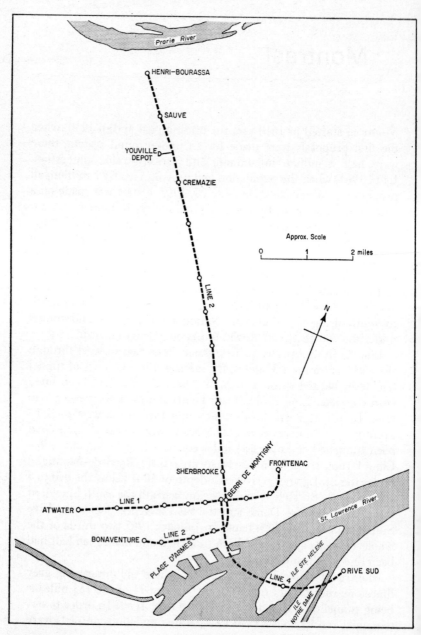

MONTREAL

let and for such small jobs elaborate mechanization would not have been economical. In general the drillers worked from temporary platforms drilling 10 ft into the rock and loading in 250 lb of dynamite. Progress is rapid covering some 35 ft in a day with about 2000 men employed round the clock, but where a seam of clay was encountered close to Atwater the speed was reduced to a yard a day.

Because of the uneven ground the depth of the line varies considerably and in places where there is a depth of soil, cut and cover methods have been used. In order to avoid the worst of the interference with street traffic, the lines have been built under secondary streets close to and parallel with the main thoroughfares. The crossing of the south river by Line 4 was made in the summer and autumn of 1964 by building dams across the river and working in an open trench.

The running tunnels are 23 ft 4 in wide and 16 ft 3 in high, opening out to 44 ft width for the 26 stations, which were generally built by cut and cover. They are spaced from 1600 ft apart in the central area to one mile in the outlying parts. All will have platforms 500 ft long, for nine-car trains, with sub-surface booking halls and entrances within buildings, rather than from the pavements. There will be 125 escalators and nowhere will passengers be required to climb more than 12 ft by stairs. Passenger traffic will be strictly one way and controlled by automatic gates. Berri-de-Montigny will be a three-level station with Line 1 below Line 2, and Line 4 alongside.

Many of the stations only require equipment and finishings and it is hoped to open Line 1 and at least the portion of Line 2 between Cremazie and Place d'Armes by the autumn of 1966. Track is already being laid on either side of Cremazie, work has also started upon the maintenance depot at Youville between Cremazie and Sauve and upon the central control office south of Sherbrooke, on Berri Street. Line 4 is to open early in 1967 in time for the World Fair.

After Paris, Montreal is the world's largest French-speaking city and therefore it is not surprising that the Paris Metro has been taken as a model for 'Le Métro de Montreal' and engineers of R.A.T.P. have constantly been visiting and giving technical advice. The rolling stock is being built in the Montreal plant of

Canadian Vickers and utilizes over 80 per cent Canadian material as well as items from France, Britain and Sweden.

The Paris system of pneumatic-tyred bogies has been adopted with little change. This has a particular advantage of better adhesion than steel-tyred stock, enabling gradients of up to 1 in 16 to be used, and allowing the tracks to dip down steeply from shallow stations to the depth where the rock is good for rapid and economical tunnelling.

The description of the Paris Metro rubber-tyred stock on a later page will give a good idea of the main features. Trains of nine cars are to run at $1\frac{1}{2}$-minute intervals in the peak hours, each train consisting of three units of permanently coupled motor, trailer and motor. Each unit is 166 ft $8\frac{1}{2}$ in long over couplings, the motors being 56 ft 5 in and the trailer 53 ft $10\frac{1}{2}$ in long with a width of 8 ft 3 in, height of 12 ft 0 in, and weight of about 27 tons per motor and 20 tons per trailer. Lateral seating is provided for 40 and room for 120 standing in each car. The seats are on a resilient frame with foamed rubber upholstery covered in a synthetic material. Lighting is by two rows of fluorescent tubes. Heaters beneath the seats, and in air intake ducts, are thermostatically controlled, air being exhausted by fans in the roof. Four pairs of doors each side give clear openings 4 ft 3 in wide.

The 369 cars, 246 motors and 183 trailers are powered by 150-h.p. motors working on 720 V d.c. Each driven bogie carries two motors set longitudinally and driving through double reduction differential gears of automobile type. Braking is rheostatic with balanced air braking operating through shoes of impregnated beech wood on the steel-tyred safety wheels. Acceleration will be up to 3 m.p.h. per second and the top speed 50 m.p.h.

The track is similar to that in Paris, with 'safety' rails at the normal 4 ft $8\frac{1}{2}$ in gauge, wide concrete tracks at 6 ft $6\frac{1}{2}$ in centres and conductor-guide rails 8 ft $2\frac{1}{2}$ in. apart.

Moscow

Moscow became the capital city of Russia when the Union of Soviet Socialist Republics was established in 1917, but at that time it was still largely composed of a sprawling settlement of serf dwellings clustered around the 12th-century fortress of the Kremlin, in which the government offices were set up. The Kremlin is a small city in its own right with three magnificent cathedrals in which the Czars were christened, crowned and buried, and which are now used as museums. It has suffered little change over the centuries, but during the last 40 years the rest of Moscow has developed in a manner unique among the major cities of the world. A few ancient monuments such as the ornate Cathedral of St. Basil remain, but there were no large areas of architectural or antiquarian interest to interfere with planning, which is complete to a degree which would be quite impossible in cities where centuries of haphazard growth have already imposed a random pattern. Offices, shops and factories are widely dispersed among exceptionally broad boulevards laid out in a series of roughly concentric circles with other wide thoroughfares radiating outwards like the spokes of a wheel. Many of these comprise as many as six traffic lanes each way, and with only about 100,000 cars among the population of $6\frac{1}{2}$ million, there is no road congestion as other great cities know it but, surprisingly, the overall speed of road traffic is not exceptionally high.

The Metropolitan Railway has been similarly planned as a unified whole, instead of growing piecemeal as other underground systems have done. This initial operating advantage is enhanced by the fact that the majority of Muscovites work on a two- or three-shift system, and thus the worst excesses of peak hour travel are avoided. Because it is not subjected to the same strains of overloading, followed by uneconomic periods of slack traffic, the Moscow Metro is better able to provide the State with a good rate of interest on the capital sunk in its construction.

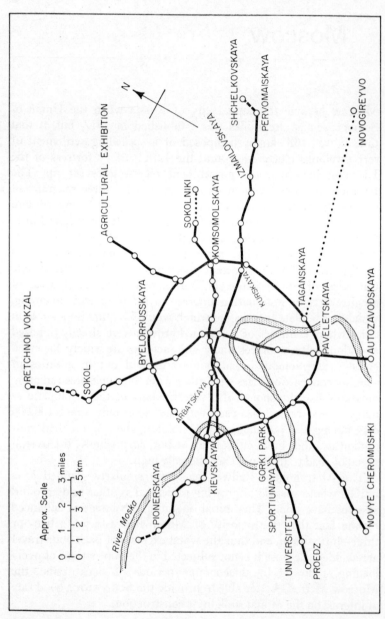

MOSCOW

Approx. Scale

0 1 2 3 miles
0 1 2 3 4 5 km

River Moska

RETCHNOI VOKZAL

SOKOL

AGRICULTURAL EXHIBITION

SOKOLNIKI

KOMSOMOLSKAYA

SHCHELKOVSKAYA

PERVOMAISKAYA

IZMAILOVSKAYA

NOVOGIREYVO

BYELORRUSSKAYA

KURSKAYA

TAGANSKAYA

PAVELETSKAYA

AUTOZAVODSKAYA

ARBATSKAYA

KIEVSKAYA

GORKI PARK

SPORTIUNAYA

UNIVERSITET

PROEDZ

NOVYE CHEROMUSHKI

PIONERSKAYA

N

The Metro carries about three million passengers a day, compared with some three and a half million on surface transport. The authorities appear to encourage the use of the Metro for longer distances and surface transport for shorter journeys by a comparatively low fare for any distance on the Metro and a sliding scale for distance, with a lower minimum, on surface transport. These arrangements, combined with the time occupied in getting up and down from the deep tube stations, have achieved the desired effect.

The large 'M' sign is the counterpart of London Transport's 'Bull's-eye' and marks every station entrance but, apart from this, direction signs and station name signs are noticeably few.

The stations themselves are remarkably clean, due to such factors as the prohibition of smoking anywhere on the system, the use of rheostatic braking, and the fact that not only station platforms, but the running tunnels are washed down twice a week. This cleanliness is emphasized by the absence of advertisements, combined with the lavish use of high intensity lighting. On the other hand, the older stations are of sumptuous design. Walls are clad in marble, or given over to some elaborate mural, ceilings are heavily embossed, and much of the lighting (at $8\frac{1}{2}$ to 11 foot-candles) comes from chandeliers. Even illuminated panels of stained glass can be found in one or two places. More recent stations, however, are receiving a less florid, more functional treatment.

The total staff numbers over ten thousand, of which a majority are women. There are many female drivers and assistant drivers on the trains, often with high school education, and positions up to that of stationmaster are open to them, in fact all but about five per cent of operating staff are women. Station women are posted at the top and bottom of every escalator and show no hesitation in stopping the machine if any passenger appears to be having trouble with luggage or any other difficulty. On the platform well-disciplined girls in distinctive red caps dispatch each train by holding up a red disc signal.

Owing to the absence of excessive crowds in the peak periods, and to the smart work of the station women, the station stops are unusually short and regular, enabling trains to run to an overall schedule of 37 to 40 km/h (23 to 25 m.p.h.) and they run at $1\frac{1}{2}$-minute intervals.

The present system comprises three through routes, a circle line linking them together and connecting to the main line railway termini, and two short radial spurs running outwards from the circle.

Construction was started in 1932, and the east–west sub-surface (cut and cover) line between Sokolniki and Gorki Park (the Park of Culture) was opened on May 15, 1935. A sub-surface line between Avbatskaya and the Kievskaya main line terminus was opened at the same time, but this line with its two miles of track, four stations and river bridge was abandoned in 1953 when a parallel deep-level tube line was brought into use between Kievskaya and another main line terminus at Kurskaya.

The first tube line (constructed like the remaining tubes at a depth of 30 to 50 m, or about 100 to 160 ft) was brought into service in 1943. It runs approximately from north to south between a surface maintenance depot at Sokol and Autozavodskaya (previously known as the Stalin Factory).

The Circle Line (also tube) was built in three stages: 1950, the southern section between Kievskaya and Kurskaya via Gorki Park and Paveletskaya; 1952, the north-eastern section running from Kurskaya to Byelorusskaya on the Sokol line with interchange facilities to the surface line at Komsomolskaya; and 1954, the circle completed between Byelorusskaya and Kievskaya. Also in 1954 the Kievskaya-Kurskaya tube, which had been built the previous year to a terminus at Ismailovskaya, was extended at ground level by using the service lines between Ismailovskaya and the surface depot of Pervomaiskaya, converting three of the depot lines into a passenger station, and this has now been extended 1·75 km to a station on the Schelkov Highway.

The next development, in 1957, was the extension from Gorki Park to Sportivnaya, and this line has recently been taken on through the University district to Proedz, the last two stations being opened in 1963. In 1958 the two radial spurs from the Circle Line to the Agricultural Exhibition and to Noviye Cheremushki were added, and in the following years the radial extension from Kievskaya to Pionerskaya was opened in stages.

The system now comprises 103½ route km (64½ miles) with the longest and oldest line, Sokol to Avtozavodskaya, extending for 20 km (12 miles). Extensions already under construction from Sokol and Pionerskaya will add a further 10·5 km (7 miles) and

Plate 33 MOSCOW *Krasnopresnen station exterior. The M sign on the roof is the only indication that this vast mausoleum is a Metro station.*

Plate 34 MOSCOW *Chandeliers and murals at Kiev Circle Line station.*

Plate 35 MOSCOW *Mayakovski station, named after the poet, has such an airy appearance that it is hard to believe it is below ground.*

Plate 36 NAGOYA *Trains are of three car units with a through corridor. The simple, well proportioned design of the rolling stock is typical of this very modern system.*

Plate 37 NAGOYA *Sakaemachi station is spacious and noticeably free of clutter and unnecessary adornment.*

Iate 38 NEW YORK *A Flushing Line train of the new Interborough rolling stock at Grand Central ation. Because of the small size of the old Interborough tunnels, the cars are noticeably smaller and orter than on other American systems.*

Plate 39 OSAKA *View from driver's cab. The complete protection of the top contact rail is noteworthy and also the thrust blocks fitted to the outside of the running rails. These are a common feature of Japanese permanent way design.*

Plate 40 OSAKA *The maintenance depot at Asashiobashi on Line 4 where trains enter to the first floor for inspection and overhaul.*

Plate 41 OSAKA *Shin-Osaka station. The fluorescent chandeliers form a pleasant feature and give good shadowless lighting.*

Plate 42 OSLO *The method of supporting the current rail in its insulation is shown, on the right, with the cover removed from the rail. On the left the polyester-glass fibre cover is in place.*

Plate 43 PARIS *The pneumatic tyred bogie seen from above.*

Plate 44 PARIS *Chaussee d' Antin Station as modernized with showcases displaying goods and con*
tinuous benches.

Plate 45 PHILADELPHIA *The newest cars are of stainless steel and have air suspension. This photo*
graph shows very clearly the normal American safety precaution of collapsible lattice type gates to fill th
space between the cars. This saves passengers from the danger of being pushed between the cars when
crowd is boarding at a station.

four more stations. Extensions are planned, and probably started before this book is published, from Sokolniki for 2 km (1¼ miles) and eastwards from Taganskaya for 13½ km (8½ miles). Another extension southwards from Autovadskaya may add another 8½ km (5¼ miles) by 1968, to raise the total length of the system to 152½ km (95 miles). The system is already the fourth largest in the world and carries the second greatest volume of traffic, estimated at over a thousand million journeys a year.

The tunnels have been driven through a fissured limestone containing a considerable quantity of water. This thick bed of limestone lies below a layer of Jurassic clay and a surface layer of glacial drift, and in some places it has deteriorated into a form of red marl which is considered to be destructive to cast iron. Consequently experiments have been made with a concrete block construction, using a ring of 10 segments 1 m wide and ¼ m (9·85 in) thick. This concrete lining is not so easy to build to correct line, and the interior diameter of the lining was increased to 5·6 m (18 ft 4 in) necessitating an excavation of 6·1 m (20 ft) diameter.

To accommodate the 5 ft gauge (the standard gauge throughout the Soviet Union) the minimum internal diameter of the tunnels is 5½ m (18 ft). This enables rolling stock of a normal subsurface type to be used with the wheels completely below floor level, but compared with the 12 ft diameter of the older London tubes the cost of excavation is doubled and the weight, or cost, of lining is half as much again.

The tubes themselves are generally lined with cast iron rings of 14 segments and a key, each ring having a width of 1 m. Though bigger than the London type of segment, they are thinner and, with the greater elbow room in the larger tunnel, there is no difficulty in erecting them.

Construction has been undertaken by the Metrostoe direct labour organization. The work has been extensively mechanized with rotary shields and an overhead conveyor at the face which takes the spoil back overhead to the skips, leaving the lower level unobstructed for the delivery of segments. Above ground the arrangements for removing spoil to tips are more elaborate than would be possible in a more densely built up city where private property has stronger claims to preservation.

The stations are unusually spacious. A typical station has two platforms, each about 15 ft wide in twin tunnels of about 30 ft diameter. Between these there is a concourse some 27 ft wide running the complete length of the platforms (160 m or 525 ft) and connected with them by numerous openings. The cut and cover sub-surface stations are also of the island type, with two rows of pillars, each only about 2 ft square, and set back about 10 ft from the platform edge with an equal width between them.

Every tube station has escalators, many of which are of exceptional length. For example, the 12 stations on the Circle Line are equipped with 82 escalators whose combined length is about 7 km ($4\frac{1}{2}$ miles). They are inclined at an angle of 30 degrees and run at 0·75 m/s (146 ft/min) which is the normal arrangement throughout the world, but their capacity of 8000 passengers per hour is rather lower than average because of a slightly narrower tread. The standard finish for the casings is wood veneer with stainless steel trimmings, and the treads are of golden brown plastic with a renewable nosing of black plastic.

The track itself is laid in much the same manner as that employed in the London tube: timber sleepers set in a concrete invert with a dished centre. The 50 kg/m (101 lb/yd) flat-bottomed rails are welded into lengths of 200 m (approximately 656 ft) and laid upon flat steel baseplates with a synthetic rubber plastic baseplate interposed. They are fastened down by a simple bent steel clip on each side which extends over the width of the baseplate and is secured by two coach screws passing through the clip and baseplate into the sleeper.

A third rail system of 850 V d.c. using underside contact is employed. The conductor rail is carried on brackets beyond the sleeper ends and is boxed in with timber throughout the running lines, sidings and station grounds where it is placed beneath the platform edge.

Signalling is by automatic colour lights with trainstops and up to four home signals, but speed control approach signalling is not used as it is thought that drivers would tend to make a brake application whenever they saw a red signal, thus defeating the object of securing the controlled non-stop entry to each station. Consideration is being given to replacing fixed signals by a system of cab signalling, similar to that used in Stockholm, and since 1962 three trains have been running in normal service under a system of automatic control. Precise details of the working of the controls is not available. There are pick-up coils over the rails on the front of the train which pick up impulses or frequencies from the track, as in cab-signalling systems. The driver has a panel of push buttons and visual indicators and it seems that a pair of buttons and one indicator refers to each section of line between two stations. There is a revolution counter on the leading axle and a time counter operating through a device which compares the time interval with the position of the train, and the control operations seem to be dictated by a pre-set programme retained on ferrite cores in the train equipment.

The rolling stock consists of 106 trains each of 6 cars with 64 spares, a total of 700 cars. The cars are of all-steel construction, painted light blue above the waist rail and dark blue below. They are 19 m (62 ft 4 in) long, 2·75 m (9 ft 0 in) wide, and 3·75 m (12 ft 4 in) high above the rail. The bogies have a wheel base of 2·5 m (8ft 2in) and 13 m (42 ft 7 in) between centres. They are all welded, and the newer type carry two fully suspended lightweight motors each driving an axle by a flexible jointed shaft. Rheostatic braking is used with air brakes of the Westinghouse type and non-metallic blocks. The presence of both the driver and assistant driver in the cab is thought to render a 'dead man's handle' unnecessary. The whole mechanical design aims at cutting out elaboration and re-finements in favour of simplicity and reliability. The newest E type stock is designed for a maximum speed of 90 km/h (56 m.p.h.) with 4 km/h (2·5 m.p.h.) per second acceleration and a braking rate of 4·7 km/h (3 m.p.h.) per second and in order to decrease noise the wheels have plastic inserts between the tyre and the disc. The interior of the cars is generally to a utility standard with leather-covered seats all facing inwards, hand rails chromium plated, and tungsten lighting with an intensity at reading level of about $4\frac{1}{2}$ to $5\frac{1}{2}$ foot-candles. The four double doors on each side open automatically to provide a gap of 1·3 m (4 ft $4\frac{1}{2}$ in). The average load per car is 170 passengers (44 seated). The permitted maximum is 250 per car, giving a capacity for the usual six-car train of between a thousand and fifteen hundred passengers (although eight-car trains are also operated). On each train there is a compartment reserved for old people, the disabled, and expectant mothers.

The stock is maintained from three depots at Sokol, Krasnoselskaya and Pervomaiskaya. Cars receive detailed examination after each run of 6000 km (3720 miles); running repairs at 32,000 km (19,800 miles); body lifting at 200,000 km (124,000 miles); and complete overhaul at 600,000 km (372,000 miles), or about once every three years. Winter conditions render it necessary to stable all rolling stock under cover. Heating pipes are built into the depot pits, and the entrances of sheds are protected by a curtain of warm air blown upwards and outwards from a trough in the door sill in order to keep out the snow.

Nagoya

Nagoya was founded in 1610 when the Shogun built a castle for his son upon the Shonai river close to the large land-locked Ise Bay on the eastern, Pacific, shore of Japan. A community developed under the protection of the castle, but this was so disorganized that it could not be called a city until 1889 when a municipality was formed and planning was not in evidence until the City Planning law was passed in 1924.

The city now ranks as the third largest in Japan with a population of nearly 2 million in an area of 122 square miles. It had become one of the country's largest centres of the munition industry and was very severely damaged in the last war. In 1946 a drastic replanning was started, but this suffered a severe set-back from a typhoon in September 1959 which caused enormous damage to property and many casualties, in a city which had not previously experienced such a disaster.

In 1954 plans were produced for a system of 75·2 km (47 miles) of which 14·8 km (9¼ miles) are already complete or nearing completion.

Line 1 was opened from Nagoya main line station eastwards to the city centre at Sakaemachi (2·63 km) in November 1957, from Sakaemachi to Ikeshita (3·45 km) in June 1960, to Higashiyama Koen (2·6 km) in April 1963 and during 1965 it is to be extended to Hoshigaoka (1½ km). The remaining 8½ km (5¼ miles) of this 18·5-km (11½ mile) line have not yet been started upon.

Line 2 is to run from Ozone in the north through Sakaemachi to Tsukijiguchi in the harbour area, a distance of 14·4 km (9 miles) and the first 4·9 km (3½ miles) from Shiya Kushomae to Kanayama is to be opened in 1966.

The stations have extensive sub-surface concourses containing shops and the booking hall, from which stairways lead down to wide island platforms 100 to 112 m (325 to 367 ft) long and 9 m to 11 m (29 to 36 ft) across.

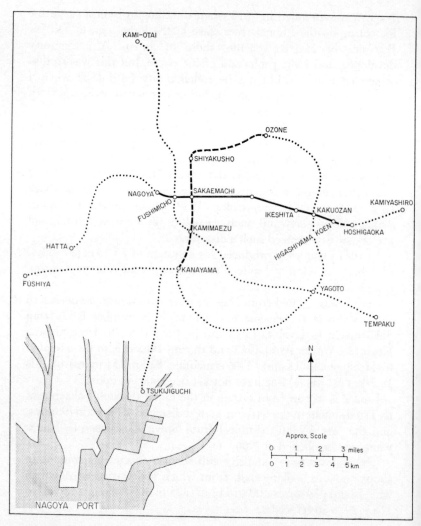

KAMI-OTAI

OZONE

SHIYAKUSHO

NAGOYA   SAKAEMACHI

FUSHIMICHO

KAMIMAEZU   IKESHITA   KAKUOZAN   KAMIYASHIRO

HATTA   HIGASHIYAMA KOEN   HOSHIGAOKA

FUSHIYA   KANAYAMA

YAGOTO

TEMPAKU

N

TSUKIJIGUCHI

Approx. Scale

0   1   2   3 miles

0   1   2   3   4   5 km

NAGOYA PORT

NAGOYA

The lower station design is simple but attractive with a row of massive cylindrical pillars on either side of a central concourse, and a refreshing absence of irrelevant decoration. Three continuous rows of fluorescent lights set in the flat ceiling give a good shadow-free illumination.

Trains of three cars run throughout the day but it is intended to enlarge them to 6 cars for the rush-hour as traffic develops from the present level of about 75 million passengers a year. With an average station stop of 20 seconds the scheduled speed is 32·3 km/h (20 m.p.h.) and the headway is 2 minutes in the rush-hour and 4 minutes in the off-peak period. The fare is a flat rate of 20 yen for any distance and almost exactly half the passengers hold season tickets.

Much of the city lies below sea level, as much as four feet below, with the highest point only 368 feet above, and the subsoil is of water bearing silt. Consequently the tunnels were built by cut and cover methods under the wide streets in the form of rectangular boxes with a central row of pillars between the two tracks. Between Ikeshita and Kakuozan the line passes under property and is in a double track concrete tube.

The track gauge is 1·435 m (4 ft 8½ in) with 50 kg/m (101 lb/yd) flat-bottomed rails on wooden sleepers and a third rail carrying the 600 V d.c. traction current. The maximum gradient is 1 in 30 and the minimum radius 125 m (410 ft). Signalling is of the conventional automatic block type with colour lights and trainstops.

The fleet of rolling stock comprises 60 cars, made up into three-car trains with intermediate corridor connections. Sixteen of these trains are normally in service with four spares, and when all are idle the depot at Ikeshita is full to capacity. Each car seats 36 on longitudinal seats with room for 80 standing. On each side three single doors provide openings of 1·1 m (3 ft 6 in). The length over couplings is 15·58 m (51 ft 1 in), the width 2·5 m (8 ft 3 in), height from rail 3·43 m (11 ft 3 in) and the weight is 22 tons. The 30-in diameter wheels have rubber sheets fitted on both sides to deaden noise.

Line 3 of the plan is to be built between Kami–Otai in the north to Tempaku in the south-east, a distance of 18·2 km (11½ miles) crossing Line 1 at Fushimicho and Line 2 at Kamimaezu. Line 4 consists of a semicircle of 16·8 km (10½ miles) from Ozone, the northern terminus of Line 2, past Higashiyama Koen on Line 1 and Yagoto on Line 3, to Kanayama on Line 2. Line 5 extends this from Kanayama to Fushiya. The plan is well established and not so liable to alteration as the schemes of other large cities, but the order of priority and date of building these lines is not yet decided.

New York

At the beginning of this century New York was served by a net-work of elevated railways but these have been abandoned pro-gressively in favour of underground railways, until now the only two remaining sections of 'elevated' are parts of the Third Avenue and Myrtle Avenue Lines.

The New York system carries a greater volume of traffic than any other of the world's underground railways, but the total traffic by underground and surface public transport is less than that of London. The City of New York has a population of about 8 million, while the New York Metropolitan Region is inhabited by double this number or almost a tenth of the citizens of the U.S.A. It is estimated that over 9 million people enter and leave the 9 square miles of the Manhattan business district each day by all forms of transport, half of these during the rush-hours. Each weekday nearly 5 million passengers use the 486 stations of the underground systems. There are $237\frac{1}{2}$ route miles, of which 134 miles are in tunnel.

There are two types of train, the express of 11 cars and the local with eight cars. The express has a scheduled overall speed of 20 m.p.h. stopping only at the more important stations, while the local, all station, trains average 16 to 18 m.p.h. Many of the routes have four tracks but in some cases there are three tracks, two for the locals and a third used for 'up' express trains in the morning and for 'down' traffic in the evening peak hours. The maximum number of trains per hour is 32 each way.

The double track lines with local trains only are usually built with side platforms and at the 'Express Stop' stations on four track sections island platforms are provided for interchange between the two services. Much of the system is in cut and cover with shallow stations and there are few escalators or lifts (82 escalators and 24 lifts). The older stations have separate entrances to the street from each platform which causes many passengers to cross a busy

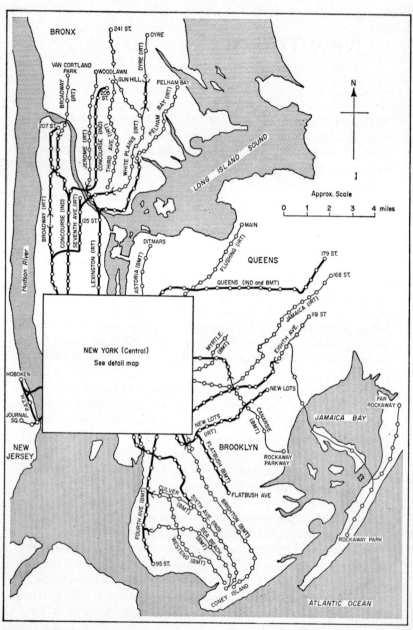

NEW YORK (General)

street to catch a train in the direction they require. Because of this, and of the saving in maintenance and operation, a sub-surface booking hall with street entrances on both sides to serve an island platform is preferred for new construction, in spite of the greater initial cost.

The oldest part of this system is the Broadway and Fourth Avenue Line, opened in 1904 and extended in 1908 towards the south-east from Manhattan to Brooklyn. This is known as the Interborough System.

The second group of lines was built between 1913 and 1920 by the Brooklyn–Manhattan Transit Company and a third, the Independent System, owned and operated by the City of New York, was constructed between 1925 and 1930.

The City of New York acquired both the older systems in June 1940 and subsequently the New York City Board of Transportation absorbed many of the tramways, bus and trolleybus routes. In June 1953 the Board of Transportation was replaced by the New York City Transit Authority who now operate the three underground systems and the remaining sections of elevated railway.

In addition to these lines of the N.Y.C.T.A. the Port Authority Trans-Hudson Corporation own and operate two routes under the Hudson river. On the New Jersey side these both join up with the main line railways, but on the New York side one terminates at Cortland Street and the other runs north under Manhattan to 33rd Street, parallel to the South Avenue Line of the Independent System. The total route mileage of double track amounts to 8 miles, and 31 million passengers are carried in a year. The tunnels are 15 ft and 18 ft diameter and the line operates on 60 V d.c.

These tubes belonged to the Hudson and Manhattan Railway Company which failed, and the responsibility for them was assumed by the Port Authority in September 1962. They now have a 150 million dollar programme for modernization to be completed by 1969.

The construction of the N.Y.C.T.A. lines is too varied for detailed description. There are the original Broadway to Fourth Avenue tunnels, 25 ft 3 in wide and 12 ft 9 in high from rail level, of box section with central supports; various forms of two, three and four track cut and cover tunnels, cast iron tube stations and

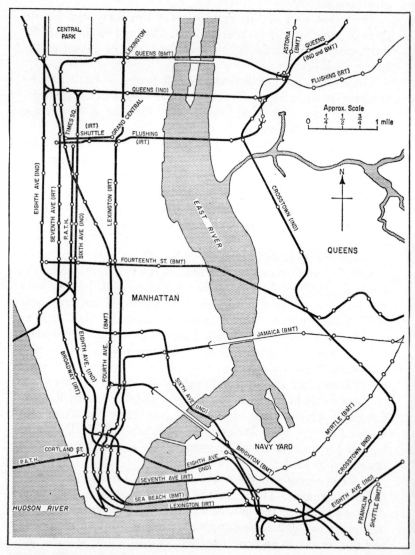

NEW YORK (Central)

16 ft 6 in diameter concrete-lined tubes built in 1930 under the East River.

Typical of the latest standards is the reconstructed Lexington Avenue station. This was built in 1918 with local trains on an upper level and limited stop trains below. In November 1962 a new deep-level station, 73 ft below the street was built with platforms 525 ft long and 14 ft wide and connected to the old Interborough local station by two high-speed escalators. From that level to the sub-surface booking hall two more high-speed escalators are provided. The station is an important interchange between the Interborough and the Queens Line of the IND and BMT systems.

The permanent way has a gauge of 4 ft 8½ in, widened to 4 ft 8⅞ in on curves of a radius less than 500 ft and to 4 ft 9 in where the radius is under 200 ft. The main line curvature is never less than 350 ft radius and check rails are used on curves of radius less than 1000 ft. There are several differing designs of track, but 100 lb/yd flat-bottomed rail is used throughout. The oldest type has the rails on steel baseplates upon impregnated pads fixed by four spikes to 6 in × 8 in × 8 ft 6 in sleepers, with 9 ft 6 in sleepers to carry the current rails. A later type is similar but in place of sleepers 6 in × 10 in timber blocks under each rail are embedded in the concrete invert.

A very novel design of track is under test over a length of half a mile, on the Times Square shuttle line beneath 42nd Street and at the three stations south of Grand Central on the Lexington Avenue line. The 39-ft long rails are fishplated together but no bolts are used, the fishplates being glued to the rails. Each rail is held by fourteen rubber mouldings, 1 ft 8·5 in long and 1·875 in thick beneath the rail, which completely encase the foot of the rail and take the place of baseplates, being bolted directly to the concrete invert.

The traction supply is by top contact on a 150-lb/yd dumbbell-shaped third rail fed from about 150 substations at 600 V d.c. The high-tension supply for the Independent lines is taken from the Consolidated Edison Company. The Brooklyn–Manhattan and the Interborough lines generate their own electricity at three power stations: on the Hudson river at Fifty-ninth Street with 205,000 kW capacity; on the East River at Seventy-fourth Street, 120,000 kW; and at Kent Avenue, 180,000 kW.

Signalling is generally by automatic block with colour light signals and trainstops, and on the Flushing Line, which served the World Fair, there is a programme machine system of train regulation very similar to that used by London Transport.

Automatic working was introduced on the Times Square to Grand Central shuttle line on January 4, 1962. The shuttle train is controlled from a dispatcher's office at the east end of the line by an electronic train dispatcher acting upon the indications of a tape which is perforated to form a programme of working for the whole day.

This dispatcher introduces electrical impulses to the running rails and these are picked up by induction in two receiving coils on the leading bogie of the train. After being amplified in the cab they are decoded to operate appropriate relays in the train control system.

A generator driven by an axle produces an a.c. voltage having a frequency proportional to the train speed at any instant. This frequency is automatically compared with that of the impulses received via the running rails and according to the result, controls are applied to the motors or brakes to give the desired acceleration, uniform speed or deceleration.

Thus the train stops in the terminal platform, the doors open, headlights and tail lights are changed over, and the destination sign is altered automatically. After a stop of one minute the doors close and the train accelerates away in the other direction.

Safety is assured by ensuring that if any one door should be open while running or before leaving the platform, the brakes are applied. Similarly, braking is effected if the speed falls below $1\frac{1}{2}$ m.p.h. as might happen with a power failure, or if the actual speed exceeds that called for by the impulses in the running rails by more than about 2 m.p.h.

The impulses are given in a.c. supply of $91\frac{2}{3}$ cycles and this is interrupted 75, 180 or 270 times a minute. The code of 75 times a minute opens the doors, but this cannot occur unless the brakes are fully on and the speed is less than $1\frac{1}{2}$ m.p.h. The 180 code corresponds to 5·6 m.p.h. and the 270 code calls for 30 m.p.h. and if no impulses are received there is a full application of the pneumatic brakes.

When a train is running correctly at 30 m.p.h. on a 270 coded section and enters a section coded at 180 impulses a minute, the immediate effect is felt in an application of both the rheostatic and the pneumatic brakes. When the speed has been reduced to 16 m.p.h. the pneumatic brake is released but rheostatic braking continues until the speed has fallen to 5·6 m.p.h. as called for by the 180 code.

The fleet of rolling stock comprises about 6700 cars of which 4600 have been introduced since 1947. Because of the smaller tunnels the cars on the older Interborough lines are limited to a length of 51 ft 4 in over couplings, 8 ft 9½ in width and a height of 11 ft 11 in. For the last 17 years renewal of rolling stock has been concentrated upon the old fleet of the Interborough Line, and all pre-war cars have now been replaced by 2850 new cars, with the exception of 50 cars purchased for the 1939–1940 World Fair.

The cars of the Brooklyn-Manhattan and Independent lines are larger and cannot be interchanged with those of the Interborough. Of the cars built before 1928 for these two lines, all have been replaced except for 397 which were completely rebuilt in 1961 and are expected to remain in service until after 1970. Since the war over 1700 new cars have been introduced on these lines and there is a settled policy of retiring cars after 35 years' service, which involves purchasing 200 new cars every year.

The latest order is for 600 stainless steel Brightliner cars which are 60 ft 6 in over couplings, 10 ft wide and 12 ft 2 in high. They accommodate 50 in longitudinal seats mouded in glass fibre plastic, have handgrips for 68 standing, and will take 220 in a crush. Four pairs of doors giving a clear opening of 46 in are offset on each side. The exterior is finished in royal blue and steel, the interior ceiling is off-white, walls and seats are in acquamarine enamel. The new cars replace the sombre hues of the old interiors with clean pastel shades and the old drab exteriors by bright reds and blues.

The car bodies are of stainless steel, coated inside with ⅛ in of latex based sound absorbent. The floor, of ¾ in plywood clad on one side with aluminium, is covered with blue-green vinyl-asbestos tiles. Ventilation is by six 3000 ft³/min fans drawing air from roof louvres and discharging through grilles in the ceiling. Thermostatically controlled dampers keep the interior at 70°F.

Each car is powered by four 100-h.p. motors driving the 34-in wheels through 7·235 to 1 helical gears and giving acceleration up to 2½ m.p.h./sec with a balancing speed of 50 m.p.h. The close spacing of stations in New York renders a high speed unnecessary and the trains are not expected to exceed 40 m.p.h. in service. Rheostatic braking operates down to 7 m.p.h. where air brakes take over, and service deceleration is at 2½ m.p.h./per second with emergency braking at 3 m.p.h. per second. The cars are in coupled pairs and capable of operation in 12 car sets. They are designed so that the roof and floor act as the flanges and the side walls as the web of a girder. By this construction and the use of stainless steel, 4 tons have been saved in weight.

Tests are in progress on a two-way radio system of communication between the central headquarters, train drivers and certain operating and police staff. Each train carries a portable two-way radio set and other staff have walkie-talkies. The test area is an 8-mile section of four-track line centred upon Grand Central Station on the Lexington Avenue Line and covering 23 stations between the junctions at 125th Street and Bowling Green in Manhattan.

There are many plans for improvement of the N.Y.C.T.A. system and much has been done in the past few years. In particular a new deep-level tunnel is under construction beneath the existing Independent line in 6th Avenue, to give the effect of four tracks and enable expresses to be run as well as stopping trains, and this should be completed in 1967. A new crossing under the East River for the Brooklyn-Manhattan line from 64th Street in Manhattan to 41st Avenue in Queens is another work just started and expected to be in service in 1971. In contrast to many systems which grow only in occasional sudden spurts, the New York underground is in a constant state of development and in the last 10 years has spent an average 80 million dollars a year, an expenditure which will increase as the years go on if all the plans contemplated are implemented.

Plate 48 ROTTERDAM *Sections of double track tunnel being built in a specially constructed dry dock on the site of a bombed department store. The dock will be flooded and the completed sections floated along purpose made canals into their final position under the main thoroughfare 'Coolsingal'.*

Plate 49 ROTTERDAM *Canal along Coolsingal being excavated. It will be filled in and the tram tracks moved back to their original position when the tunnel sections are in position.*

Plate 50 ROTTERDAM *Boys play on the roof of a tunnel section submerged in the temporary canal in the Hofplein Square. A main line train is entering Centraal station in the background.*

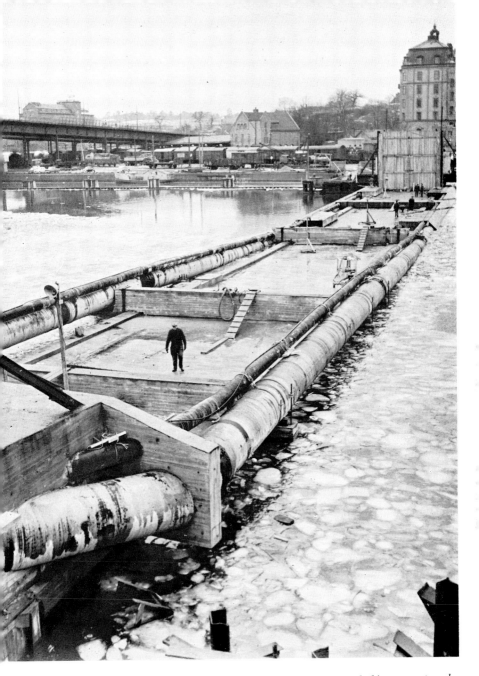

Plate 51 STOCKHOLM Trains between Hornstall and Liljeholmen travel through this concrete tunnel,
now 7 m (24 ft) below the water. The tunnel was constructed in a shipyard and towed to the site where the
photograph shows it being sunk.

Plate 52 STOCKHOLM *Tunnelling through rock by blasting. The marks of the holes, drilled to blast out the final shape of the tunnel, can be clearly seen on the finished rock face.*

Plate 53 STOCKHOLM *The upper portion of the Centralen station is decorated with a tiled wall by Anders Asterling and pillars 'carved in concrete' by Siri Kerkert. Passengers may admire these while seated on heated concrete benches designed by Egon Moller-Nielsen.*

Plate 54 TOKYO *The interior of a Tozai Line car. The wide standing space, the lavish provision of hand holds and the vestibule connections to the other cars are valuable features of this design.*

Plate 55 TORONTO *The first underground car ever built in Canada was the first car of the first train when the University Line opened on February 28, 1963. These cars are exceptionally long (nearly 75 ft) and seat 84 passengers but, owing to the extensive use of light alloys, weigh less than 27 tons.*

Plate 56 VIENNA *At Schottentor the trains reverse on two loops, one directly above the other and all the facilities of a modern interchange station are provided.*

Osaka

Osaka is the second largest city of Japan and a great seaport on the delta of the River Yodo. It originated in the late 16th century as a settlement under the protection of the strongest fortress in the country, now completely restored. In the half century up to 1940 the population increased from $\frac{1}{2}$ to $3\frac{1}{2}$ million. Then the war came and a third of the city was utterly destroyed and the population was reduced to very little more than a million. Now the destruction has been repaired, the city is expanding rapidly, and the population is again over $3\frac{1}{4}$ million.

Osaka is faced by what may prove to be the most serious traffic problem in the world. In the last five years the registration of private cars in the prefecture has increased from 190,000 to 447,000. The roads account for only 10 per cent of the total area of the city, compared with 23 per cent in London and 35 per cent in New York. The population density in thousands of persons per square mile is 41 in Osaka, $27\frac{1}{2}$ in London, $24\frac{1}{2}$ in New York and only $16\frac{1}{4}$ in Chicago. Already two-thirds of the business population live in the suburbs and this tendency is increasing even more rapidly as the population increases.

The existing underground system of Line 1 from north to south through the city, with a branch of the southern portion, Line 3, and Line 4 from the city centre to Osaka Port to the west, comprises 27 route km (17 miles) and carries over 280 million passengers a year. Work is in progress on a further 40 km (25 miles) of route to be completed about 1967, and it is intended to complete the network of 115 km (72 miles) by 1975. Line 4 runs as an elevated railway between Osaka Port and Bentencho. Line 1 comes to the surface beyond Nakatsu to cross the Yodo river on a bridge, which it shares with a wide roadway, and continues above ground to Shin-Osaka, the terminus of the National Railways' magnificent new Tokiado Line. Of the 23 stations now open all but six are underground.

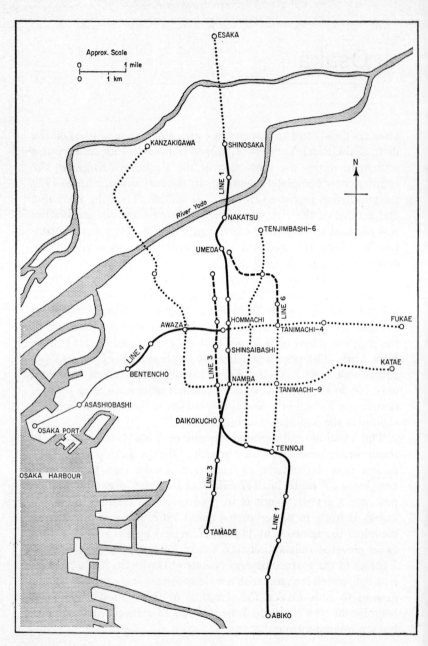

OSAKA

On Line 1 the eight-car trains run at $2\frac{1}{4}$-minute intervals in the rush-hour, and between Namba and Shinsaibashi the congestion is acute, trains designed for a thousand passengers being crammed with three thousand. On Line 4 only two-car trains are running at present, and the branch Line 3 is worked by two-car trains shuttling between Daikokucho and Tamade.

The stations vary in design but the more modern are examples of spacious and graceful planning with large sub-surface booking halls, only obstructed by highly polished round pillars, and platforms over 10 m (33 ft) wideand, on Line 1, long enough for 10-car trains, nearly 600 ft. The deeper stations have escalators for up traffic and stairways for entering passengers. The wide island platform beneath a lofty, arched roof is a feature of several stations, another is the very effective lighting by fluorescent tubes arranged as a chandelier in the form of an inverted, truncated cone. Other stations have side platforms with a flat roof, supported by columns and hidden by false ceilings in which the lighting is set flush.

Municipal transport originated in Osaka with the opening of a tramway to Osaka Port in September 1903 and developed with buses in 1927 and trolleybuses in 1953. The underground railway construction started in January 1930 and in May 1933 the first section of $3\frac{1}{4}$ km (2 miles) was opened between Umeda in the north and the busy shopping centre of Shinsaibashi. Ten single cars carried some 15,800 passengers a day. A short section of 1 km southwards to Namba followed in October 1935, and in April 1938 the line was taken south to Daikokucho and east along the main line railway to Tennoji a further $3\frac{1}{2}$ km ($2\frac{1}{4}$ miles). Three-car trains were operated and traffic went up to 90,000 a day.

In May 1942 Line 3, the branch from Daikokucho was opened to Hanazonocho for another $1\frac{1}{4}$ km ($\frac{3}{4}$ mile) to make the whole system $8\frac{3}{4}$ km ($5\frac{1}{2}$ miles) long, carrying 216,000 passengers daily in 42 cars. Construction was then suspended until June 1950. Line 1 was extended southwards to Showacho (1·8 km) in December 1951 and to Nishitanabe (1·3 km) in October 1952.

In December 1954 trains were increased to four cars between Umeda and Nishitanabe. Line 3, the branch, was taken on to Kishinosato (1·1 km) in June 1956 and to Tamade (1·2 km) in May 1958. Five-car trains had run on Line 1 since October 1957, and were made up to six cars in June 1958, while Line 3, which had run single cars, acquired two cars per train in September 1959. Seven-car trains appeared on Line 1 in July 1960 when the line was further extended to Abiko (2·5 km). Line 1 was completed to its present length of 16½ km (10¼ miles) in September 1964 by the extension northwards from Umeda to Shin-Osaka to afford interchange with the new Tokiado trunk line which runs from Osaka to Tokyo.

Line 4 was built from Osaka Port to Bentencho as an elevated railway to connect with a loop line of the National railways between December 1959 and 1961 and carried on underground from Bentencho to Hommachi on Line 1 in October 1964.

Since May 1963 work has been in progress on a 5·3-km (3⅓ mile) extension of Line 3 northwards from Daikokucho parallel with the Line I as far as Umeda, to relieve the congested centre of Line 1. Work has also started on a new Line 2 between Umeda and Tanimachi-4 over a length of 3¾ km (2¼ miles).

Except where river crossings are being built with floating caissons the tunnels are of cut and cover construction, mainly a double-track box section with a central support, but in places with an arched roof, all in reinforced concrete. They follow the line of the streets with the track between 11 and 14 m (36 to 46 ft) below ground.

The track is ballasted with 50 kg/m (101 lb/yd) flat-bottomed rails and baseplates upon timber sleepers and set to 1·435 m (4 ft 8½ in) gauge. The third rail is arranged for top contact with continuous timber protection above and to one side and carries 750 V d.c. current.

Signalling is of the normal automatic block type with colour light signals and trainstops and all trains are fitted with an inductive radio system of communication between the driver and the central control office at Tennoji station.

The 290 motor cars are painted ivory above the waist and orange below this. Inside, the newer cars look spacious, with longitudinal seating for 46 and room, officially, for 74 standing passengers and, in fact for many more in the rush-hour of the central district; but with straight sides and a somewhat flat roof they have a rather boxlike appearance. Lighting is by 40 fluorescent tubes, each of 40 watts, enclosed in white translucent shades, set above the seats at the sides and along the centre of the car. Ventilation is by louvres on a raised longitudinal section of the double roof and ten fans behind circular ventilators in each ceiling. On each side there are three double doors operated by the guard, and providing openings of 1·3 m (4 ft 3 in). Four loudspeakers in each car are connected to a fully transistorized public address system.

The bulk of the newer rolling stock consists of 50 cars coupled into two-car units. Each car is 18 m (59 ft) long, 2·89 m (9 ft 6 in) wide and 3¾ m (12 ft 3 in) from rail level. Each car carries a compressor; one has the control gear and weighs 35 tons, while the other with the motor generator set weighs 36 tons. The six newest cars are single units, each with four 120-h.p. motors with 23 control stops (compared with 13 on the earlier cars). They weigh 36 tons, seat 48 and have room for 82 standing passengers. Wheels are of 0·86 m (33¾ in) diameter and, on the latest cars, the gear ratio has been reduced to 1 : 7·357, compared with 1 : 6·059 on the earlier.

Line 1 and 3 rolling stock is maintained in a surface depot south of Abiko and that for Line 4 in an unusual shop at Asashiobashi, near Osaka Port, into which the trains enter at first-floor level from the elevated railway track.

Future plans include, as first priority, the extension of Line 2 southwards from Tanimachi-4 to Tennoji with one intermediate station; extension of Line 4 through Tanimachi-4 eastwards for 4¼ km; a new Line 5 from the north to Awaza, Namba and the intermediate station of the Line 2 extension, Tanimachi-9, and on to the east, a total distance of 9¾ km; and another new Line 6 from north to south parallel to Lines 2 and 3 and midway between them, over a length of 7 km. Line 6 is intended to be physically connected with existing electric railways at both ends.

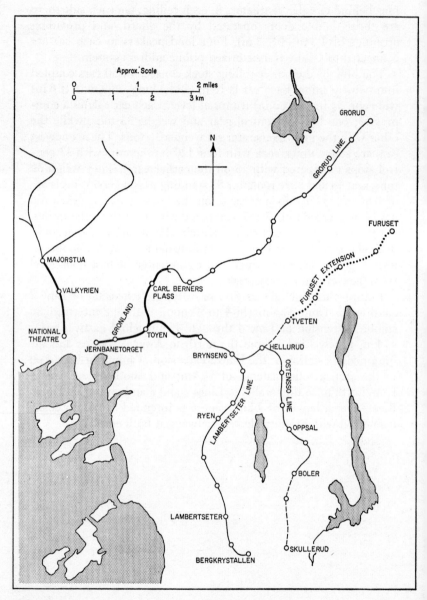

OSLO

Oslo

The Norwegian capital is over sixty miles from the sea, at the head of a deep fiord which is open to shipping even in the hardest winter. The city lies sheltered in a bowl which rises to 300 ft above sea level and is surrounded by forest clad hills 1200–1500 ft high. For many years the population, now close upon half a million, has been served by a system of trains and light railways reaching out to the forests and ski-ing slopes.

The first light railway was opened in 1898, and in 1912 the north-western fan of lines, which focuses upon Majorstua, was to be connected to the city centre by an underground section. Delay was caused by difficult ground and by failure to agree upon the site of the city terminus. Then in 1914 a serious subsidence occurred leaving the train lines suspended in the air. Work was stopped and construction was delayed until 1926 owing to lawsuits occasioned by damage to structures through blasting out rock, soil investigations of the strata of rock and weak clay, and efforts to raise more capital. At last, on June 27, 1928, King Haakon opened the line from Majorstua to the National Theatre, a distance of 1·96 km (1¼ miles) with one intermediate station, Valkyrien.

By 1945 there was considerable building on the eastern side of the city and it was clear that the existing light railways would be inadequate for the traffic. The city founded its own underground organization in 1949 and obtained approval of a plan in 1954. This provides for two branch lines, to be built on the existing alignment of light railways, and one new section of line to be brought into the city in a common underground section. The possible connection through the city to National Theatre is not yet proposed, because the traffic to the north-west is expected to be only half that from the south and east, giving a very uneven balance, and because of the expense of raising the standard of the existing lines to that necessary in the newer sections.

The two old light railways, the Lambertseter of 6 km (3¾ miles), and Ostensjo of 5 km (3 miles), are mainly on the surface. The Ostensjo Line was extended from Oppsal to Boler in July 1958 and is now being carried on to Skullerud. The Grorud Line of $9\frac{1}{4}$ km ($5\frac{3}{4}$ miles) is already mainly constructed and includes 2484 m ($1\frac{1}{2}$ miles) of rock tunnel and 384 m ($\frac{1}{4}$ mile) of concrete tunnel. One station, Carl Berner Plass, is built entirely in rock, the ticket hall being on the same level as the platforms, to which access is gained by passages beneath the track. The work upon these three lines was expected to be completed by the end of 1965, and the construction of the new branch from Hellerud to Tventen in 1966. However, the trial running and staff training will require some time and opening dates have not been fixed. The extension from Tventen to Furuset has not yet been started.

From the junction of the Lambertseter and Ostensjo Lines at Brynseng to Toyen, is a distance of $2\frac{1}{2}$ km ($1\frac{1}{2}$ miles) and includes over a kilometer of rock and 400 m of concrete tunnel. At Toyen the Grorud branch joins them and all three share one pair of tracks to the present terminus Jernbanetorget, through 657 m of rock and 1322 m of concrete tunnel.

Tunnelling in Oslo has not been easy. As in Stockholm, ridges of rock underlie the city from south-west to north-east and between them the gullies are full of a clay of low shear strength and liable to flow. The rock itself is full of faults where falls are possible and the clay may intrude. So far as possible the route has been located along the rock ridges but it is often necessary to pass through the deep inclusions of clay which vary in width from 160 to 390 m (525 to 1280 ft). Just east of Gronland station it was necessary to excavate a short section under water to obviate the danger of the trench bottom being lifted by earth stresses and the concrete tunnel was, in part, cast under water.

The rock tunnels are 9 m (29 ft 6 in) wide, opened out to $9\frac{1}{4}$ m (30 ft 4 in) on curves of less than 1 km radius, with vertical walls 3·76 m (12 ft 3 in) high and an arched roof reaching to 4·95 m (16 ft 3 in) above rail level on the straight and 5·05 m (16 ft 7 in) on curves. In weaker ground concrete box-section tunnels are used with a wall between the tracks. The height is 4·15 m (13 ft 7 in) minimum above rail level and each track has a clear width of 4·45 m (14 ft 7 in) on the straight, 4·6 m (15 ft 1 in) on curves of a radius less than 500 m and 4·75 m (15 ft 7 in) for radii under

200 m. In the open the distance between track centres is 4 m (13 ft
2 in).

The line was originally intended to have overhead transmission
of traction current, to facilitate through operation with other lines,
but it became apparent that the traffic would require frequent
heavy trains taking too much current and a third rail system of
750 V d.c. has been adopted. The third rail is arranged for bottom
contact and is provided with an unusual top and side cover
moulded in fireproof polyester reinforced with glass fibre. The
whole method of supporting the rail and cover is interesting and is
shown in Plate 42.

It is intended to run trains of up to six cars and the station
platforms are 110 m (361 ft) long. The platforms are on either
side of the tracks, mainly because of the danger of a large number
of passengers on an island platform carrying skis, which would in-
evitably be allowed to project over the track and cause accidents.
Suburban stations have street-level booking halls with platforms
4 m (13 ft 2 in) wide and above or below according to whether the
tracks cross over or under the adjacent street. Of the central,
underground stations, Gronland is typical with sub-surface concourse, booking hall and shops. Because the crowd on the eastbound platform in the evening peak will be denser than that on
the westbound in the morning, the two sides of the station differ
in design. The eastbound platform is 5½ m (18 ft) wide and on
the westbound side the width is only 4½ m (14 ft 9 in). Further-
more, there is an escalator for the heavy outwards traffic on the
westbound side, but for the inward direction three stairways are
considered adequate for the traffic which is predominantly inwards.

The system will be signalled for 40 trains an hour, but at first
only 30 trains an hour will be run between Jernbanetorget and
Toyen in the rush-hour. The system is to be similar to that used
in Stockholm with a signal panel in the driver's cab and fixed
signals only at junctions and stations. Sections of track 200 m or
more in length will be fed with impulses corresponding to 70, 50
and 15 km per hour (44, 31 and 9 m.p.h.) and the appropriate
speed will be shown by the cab signals. If the driver does not
react correctly within five seconds, the train is stopped automatically.

The rolling stock fleet on order consists of 60 all-steel cars to work in two-car units. One car accommodates 63 and the other 60 passengers on lateral seats and both are designed for 107 standing. The length over buffers is 17 m (55 ft 9 in) and the height of 3·65 m (12 ft) is normal, but the width of 3·2 m (10 ft 6 in) is wider than on most underground systems, but the same as on the light railways of Oslo. Three double doors on each side open to 1·25 m (4 ft 1 in). The cars are designed for a maximum speed of 80 km/h (50 m.p.h.) with acceleration up to 3·6 km/hr (2¼ m.p.h.) per second and braking up to 4·86 km/hr (3 m.p.h.) per second.

Originally a central workshop was to be provided at Etterstad, between Brynseng and Helsfyr, for both the underground railway and the tramway vehicles. But when, in 1960, it was decided to increase the motor bus fleet and reduce the train service, the underground railway depot was re-located at Ryen. In the severe winter weather all stock requires covered stabling and the sheds at Ryen are designed for 120 cars.

Paris

Paris is the Immortal City of modern times, besieged, threatened and occupied in successive wars, apparently indestructible and continuing her natural growth. Surface traffic flows comparatively fast with little regard for the pedestrian, and the 2·8 million inhabitants wisely make full use of the intricate system of underground railways. The Regie Autonome des Transports Parisiens (R.A.T.P.) carries about 200 million passengers a year, of which more than half travel on the Metro.

The Metro system is an underground maze of 14 lines, of which 10 are wholly underground, and 4 have short sections of viaduct over waterways. Of the whole 169 km (105 miles) of route, 159½ km (99 miles) are underground and 9½ km (6 miles) on viaduct. There are 270 stations of which 51 serve more than one line. If one counts the stations on each line separately the total is 344, but 8 of these are closed at present.

Over the 105 miles of route, nearly twice as many journeys are made each year as over the 244 miles run by London Transport trains. On the other hand, the car miles run each year are a little over 100 million, compared with 224 million run by London Transport. This means that the average length of journey in Paris is very much shorter, as a consequence of the short distance between the stations (about ½ km or ⅓ mile), the ease of access to the shallow lines, and the danger of crossing a Parisian street.

The idea of an underground railway to relieve the streets of Paris was first mooted about 1855 and was taken seriously from 1871 after the siege of Paris by the Germans. On March 30, 1898, a law was passed approving the construction of a system of five electrical underground lines with a total length of 65 km (40 miles). The original intention was to use a track gauge of 1 m (3 ft 3⅜ in) with cars 1·9 m (6 ft 3 in) wide, but when work started it was on the basis of 1·44 m (4 ft 8¹¹⁄₁₆ in) track gauge and a load gauge 2·4 m (7 ft 10½ in) wide.

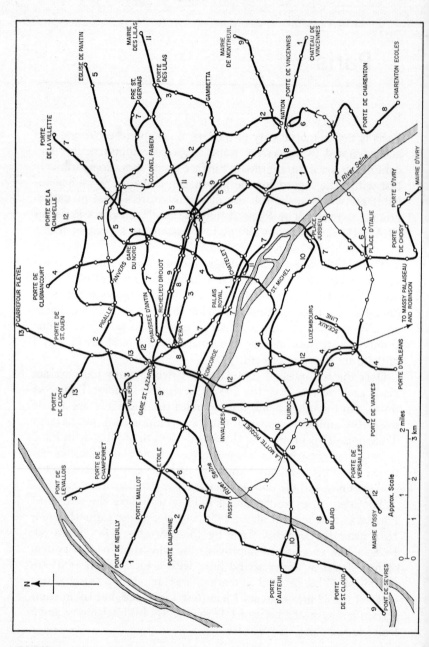

PARIS

Line 1 was the first to be opened, on July 19, 1900, between Porte Maillot and Porte de Vincennes, and by the end of that year 13·35 km (8¼ miles) and 23 stations were open, carrying over 42 million passengers a year.

By 1905 there were 30 km (18½ miles) consisting of Line 2 between Nation and Porte Dauphine, Line 3 from Villers to Gambetta, and a first portion of Line 6 from Etoile to Passy, all completely underground except for Line 2 between Anvers and Colonel Fabien.

Between 1905 and 1911 the length was extended to 82 km (51 miles) by the construction of Line 4 from Porte de Clignancourt to Porte d'Orleans, Line 5 from Gare du Nord to Place d'Italie, Line 7 between Opera, Pre St. Gervais and Porte de la Villette, Line 12 between Pigalle and Porte de Versailles, and Line 13 from Porte de St. Ouen to Gare St. Lazare. Line 3 was extended from Villers to Porte Champeret and Line 6 from Passy to Nation.

In the ten years 1911 to 1920 the growth of the system was retarded by war and only 16 km (10 miles) were added. Line 3 was completed from Gambetta to Porte des Lilas. Line 7 was extended from Opera to Palais Royal. Line 8 was built from Opera to Porte d'Auteuil, running over the tracks now used by Line 10 from La Motte Picquet to Porte d'Auteuil.

Line 9 was opened from Port de St. Cloud to Chaussee d'Antin in 1923 and extended to Richelieu-Drouet in 1928. Line 8 was also extended from Opera to Richelieu-Drouet in 1928, and carried on to Pore de Charenton in 1931. Line 7 was extended in that year from Palais Royal to Port d'Ivry and Line 10 was added, running from Invalides to Place Jussieu, over the tracks now used by Line 14 between Invalides and Duroc. The system was then 128 km (80 miles) long and lying entirely within the city boundary.

Lines 7 and 10 belonged to the Nord-Sud railway until the Metro absorbed them in 1930, and in 1942 the Metro took over the operation of the city's bus services. It was not until the first day of 1949 that the R.A.T.P. (formed in 1948) took control of all passenger transport for the city.

Since 1938 the Metro has operated the Sceaux Line from Luxembourg to Massy-Palaiseau & Robinson over a distance of 20 km (12½ miles). This is an extension of the S.C.N.F. national main line, from St. Remy-les-Chevreuse, and is built to main-line standards with full-size rolling-stock operating from an over-head system of 1500 V d.c. and carrying about 40 million passengers a year.

The stations follow many designs and the style and materials of decorative treatment differ greatly, but since 1952 there has been an extensive programme of reconstruction of the more important stations, and of the installation of fluorescent lighting. In general, side platforms are the rule, 75 m (246 ft) long on older stations, and 105 m (344 ft) on the newer lines, all about 4 m (13 ft 2 in) wide with stairs leading to sub-surface booking halls. The deeper stations have escalators or, in some cases, lifts which are rapidly being replaced by escalators.

Passengers entering and leaving the station are segregated between the booking hall and the platforms, and sliding gates at the platform entrances are used to control crowds and to prevent last-minute entry while the train is at a platform.

On the Metro there is one fare, irrespective of distance travelled, and books of ten tickets can be bought, valid from any station to any station. There is always one first-class carriage in the centre of the train, and the stopping-places of this carriage are indicated by signs on the platforms. First-class journeys cost half as much again as second class, but second-class tickets are valid in first-class cars before 8 a.m. On the Sceaux line fares vary with distance. On the Metro tickets are inspected at the entrance, on the Sceaux line at entrance and exit, and on both there are travelling inspectors. Tourist tickets, available for seven days' first-class travel by Metro, Sceaux Line or buses, are sold at banks in the principal cities all over the world, at the cost of about 24 journeys on the Metro.

The service operates from 5.30 a.m. to 1.15 a.m. with from 30 to 35 trains an hour in the peak period, each of four, five or six cars, except on the short Line 14 where three car trains run at a maximum of 25 an hour. With the stations so closely spaced, averaging 521 m (0·3 mile) apart, the schedule speed does not exceed 25½ km/h (16 m.p.h.)

The lines generally terminate in reversing loops and the terminal stations have two platforms, one for arrival and one for departure, but at five terminal stations the platforms are on either side of the single loop line and one is for alighting and the other for boarding the trains. There are also a number of intermediate stations which have loop lines, used for reversing or stabling trains in the off-peak period. These and the terminal stations are well provided with underground sidings.

The earlier lines were designed to be as close to the surface as possible, while keeping the maximum gradient at 1 in 25. The running tunnels are of horseshoe shape 7·1 m (23 ft 4 in) wide and 4·5 m (14 ft 9 in) from rail level. The stations were built in tunnels of completely elliptical shape with a major axis of 14·14 m (46 ft 5 in) and a minor axis of 5·9 m (19 ft 4 in) which gives a height of 5·2 m (17 ft) above rail level.

In places such as the under-river crossings at Chatelet and Concorde the tunnels were driven in compressed air by shields and built of iron segments lined with concrete to an interior diameter of 8 m (26 ft 3 in). Close to the river, as at St. Michel, it was necessary to sink caissons to construct the station.

With the exception of Lines 1 and 11, the track is of the conventional type having a gauge of 1·44 m (4 ft 8⅝ in). The 52 kg/m (105 lb/yd) flat-bottomed rails are 18 m (59 ft) long and laid directly upon steel baseplates with timber sleepers on a ballasted formation. Rail joints are staggered by one sleeper space on the straight and by half a rail length on curves.

The third rail is also of 52 kg/m section and is supported in insulators on the sleeper ends. It is delivered in 22 m (72 ft) lengths and continuously welded on site by the thermit process. Contact is on the top and no protection planking is used, but on rising gradients in the open, resistance cables are provided to heat the rails in severe winter weather.

Signalling is of the conventional, automatic block type, fully track circuited with two aspect colour lights and no trainstops. Repeating signals, yellow and green, are used where the sighting distance would be inadequate, and three aspects on the home signals of busy stations. Line 1 is being equipped with an automatic system by which an indicator at each station tells the driver whether to drive faster, or slower, or to wait in the station according to the headway to the preceding train, and the drivers are in direct telephonic communication with the central control.

An interesting experiment was made in 1956 with an approach

to the problems of automatic driving by a system very different from those now in use. A single continuous wire was laid between the running rails in the form of a rectangular zigzag, alternately running parallel to the rail on either side and crossing over at right angles. This track wire was fed with alternating current and a pair of induction coils were mounted on the train so as to run close above the parallel portions of the wire, alternately over a portion of wire and over a blank space. Thus a series of pulses were induced on the train wiring with a frequency proportional to the speed of the train and to the number of times the track wire crossed over in a given distance.

On the train there was a generator producing internal pulses of a fixed frequency. The induced frequency was automatically compared with the internal frequency and the train speed was controlled to keep them equal by braking or acceleration. It will be seen that if the track wire crossed over at short intervals the required frequency would be induced at a low train speed and, if there was a long distance between the crossing over, the train speed would be high. Thus by altering the spacing of the zigzag on different sections of the track, the train speed could be controlled and a gradual alteration would produce a graded increase or decrease in speed. When the wire ceased to cross over or carried no current the train would stop. At any one place two or more track wires could be laid with different spacing of their zigzags and different controlled train speeds could be produced at that point by energizing one selected track wire. This ingenious and apparently simple apparatus was in use on part of Line 11 for a time, but it would appear that some technical difficulties have caused it to disappear.

The traction current supply system is now being extensively modernized and the voltage changed from 600 V d.c., with substations working on 10 kV, to 750 V d.c. stepped down from 15 kV. The high tension supply from Electricite de France will be taken at 63 kV, being transformed to 10 kV in the early stages of modernization and finally to 15 kV in four primary substations. The first of the new primary substations is already in service supplying 24 remotely controlled secondary substations.

On completion there will be four primary and 96 secondary substations with air-cooled transformers and silicon rectifiers of

2·3 MW capacity spaced along the lines at regular intervals of about 2 km (1¼ miles). The whole supply system is to be duplicated, two 63 kV cables supplying two transformers in the primary substations. The secondary substations will have duplicate sets of equipment and will be fed by duplicate 15 kV feeders from the primary stations.

The ancillary electrical services will operate on 380 V d.c. fed by transformers from the 15 kV supply but with emergency generators cutting in automatically in an emergency.

The fleet of rolling stock for the normal lines includes over 1300 motors and a similar number of trailers, with 40 articulated sets of three cars, 37 m (121 ft 5 in) long, which run in coupled pairs to form the six-car trains of Line 13. For the Sceaux Line there are 102 cars, of which 14 belong to the S.C.N.F., 1 diesel and 7 electric locomotives.

The most interesting feature of this system is the pneumatic-tyred train which was developed from a prototype tested from 1951 onwards on a single line shuttle service between Porte des Lilas on Line 11 and Pre St. Gervais on Line 7. This line is only 770 m (842 yd) long and is not generally shown on the maps and timetables of the Metro, though it is a useful and busy cross link.

The conversion of the permanent way of Line 11 to carry pneumatic-tyred stock was achieved in the years 1954 to 1956 without interference with the normal service except for closing traffic one hour early each night. This was possible because the original running rails were retained in the new track and the new stock could be introduced into service progressively as the old cars were gradually withdrawn, from November 1956 to October 1957.

The load-carrying pneumatic tyres run upon narrow timber or concrete tracks outside the rails and a pair of conventional steel flanged wheels is mounted upon each axle and held suspended above the rails by the inflated pneumatics. If the tyres were to become deflated the steel wheels would sink to the rails, carry the load and guide the bogie in the normal way. In normal service the bogies are guided by four smaller pneumatic-tyred wheels fixed horizontally at the corners of the bogie and arranged to run against a T-shaped guiding rail. At junction work it is necessary to have gaps in this guide rail. The flanges of the steel wheels are therefore made deep enough to make contact with the rails, though normally

L

held clear of them by the effect of the pneumatic guide wheels, and through crossing work the steel flanged wheels guide the bogie.

The T-shaped guide rails on both sides of the track are mounted upon insulators and serve as positive conductor rails with side pick-up, the return current passing through the conventional 'safety' running rails. The negative traction shoes in contact with the safety rails operate the track circuits and, to avoid the noise and wear caused by the high contact pressure required by a normal track circuit, a comparatively high track voltage of 12 V is used with a high allowable shunt resistance (1·5 ohms in place of 0·150 ohms.).

The efficiency of the contact of the shoes is tested on a special track circuit at Chatelet. If this is not operated correctly a signal is set at danger and the controller receives information specifying which bogie of the train is out of adjustment. Treadles are fixed at the same site to monitor the correct inflation of each tyre by checking the height of the steel wheels. If not correct the same stop signal operates and the controller knows which tyre is flat.

Line 11 was selected for this first full-scale test because it is only 6286 m (4 miles) long with 13 stations, and requires only 16 trains of four cars each to operate it. On account of the frequent gradients, trains are made up of one trailer and four motors with all axles driven. The stock, 54 motors and 17 trailers, was built by two competing firms and are different in many respects, although capable of being coupled and worked together.

The success on Line 11 encouraged R.A.T.P. to equip another line and Line 1, with a length of 14640 m (9 miles) and 23 stations was chosen for conversion. The new track was laid and the platforms were lengthened to take six-car trains, instead of five cars, by May 1963, and by the end of 1964 the entire rolling stock of the line had been renewed. There are now 272 pneumatic-tyred vehicles which work the line as 41 trains, each of four motors and two trailers. The next line to be converted will be Line 4 and, already, the stations have been lengthened for six-car trains instead of five cars.

On Line 1 the track through stations has been lowered by 8 in and laid in concrete because this would reduce the depth of ballast too greatly. The safety rail is secured by elastic fastenings to the concrete bed and the wheel tracks are of concrete in 17 ft 9 in lengths. Between stations the old sleepers were renewed with hardwood (azobe) and the pneumatic wheel track is formed of a broad-flanged steel beam continuously welded. The azobe tracks laid on Line 11 had been found to warp, but there are advantages in fixing auxiliary fittings to wood and this type of track is used in sidings where some unevenness is not important.

All the pneumatic-tyred cars have facing pairs of double seats set transversely for 24 passengers. On the back of these seats and on the end walls there are tip-up seats to accommodate 31 passengers in all except the driving motor cars which have only 28 tip-up seats. When these are not in use, in the peak periods, the total capacity is 166 or 159 passengers respectively. The four pairs of double doors on each side have a clear opening of 1·3 m (4 ft 3 in) and are opened individually by the passengers but closed by the guard. Laminated plastics, stainless steel, and light alloys are used extensively in the interior and the lighting is fluorescent.

Driving motors are 15·515 m (50 ft 11 in) long over headstocks and the other cars 14·79 m (48 ft 6 in) long, while all cars are 2·4 m (7 ft 10½ in) wide and 3·488 m (11 ft 5¼ in) high from rail level. The driving motor cars weigh 22¼ tons, non-driving motors 21½ and trailers 15½ tons.

Each axle of a driving bogie has an automobile type differential and reduction gear and is driven by a 140-h.p. motor, giving an acceleration of up to 4·7 km/hr (3 m.p.h.) per second. Railway type electro-pneumatic brakes operate by two oil impregnated beechwood blocks upon each of the steel safety wheels, and provide service braking of 5·25 km/hr (3·25 m.p.h.) per second and emergency deceleration of 7·25 km/hr (4·5 m.p.h.) per second.

The load-carrying tyres have an external diameter of 1·1 m (43·25 in) and are inflated to 9 kg/cm² (128 lb/in²) on the motored bogies and 6·5 kg/cm² (92 lb/in²) on the trailer cars. The guiding wheels have 17/400 tyres giving an inflated diameter of 0·55 m (21½ in) and run at a pressure of 10 kg/cm² (142 lb/in²).

Nitrogen is used to inflate all tyres to reduce the (nearly negligible) risk of fire if the tyre should be overheated by the slipping of a locked wheel. In five years' use only eight punctures have occurred and the tyres have run for 200,000 miles without any great tread wear, but the steel reinforced tyres are designed for re-treading after 20 mm (¾ in) of wear.

The safety wheels have a tread diameter of 0·88 m (34½ in) and a flange, deeper than usual, projecting 72 cm (2⅛ in).

The bogie is welded up from box sections and is suspended from the axles by rubber blocks. Secondary springing is by compound rubber and steel springs. Vertical movement is controlled by friction dampers and anti-rolling bars are fitted.

For major overhaul the bogies are loaded on flat cars and the bodies mounted on special bogies to enable them to be transported over the normal track to the main rolling stock depot at Choisy. Inspection and minor attention is given in a special section of tunnel at Lilas where a central track for body lifting and two outer tracks for minor repairs and adjustments have been built in a tunnel 180 m (590 ft) long and 11·5 m (37 ft 9 in) wide.

The articulated stock of Line 13 was introduced in 1949 ready for the extension from Porte St. Ouen to Carrefour in 1952. It is not well suited to make up trains of the maximum length accommodated by the longer stations of other lines, but well adapted to Line 13, a suburban line of 6½ km (4 miles) with 11 stations in service, having platforms only 75 m (246 ft) long, and a great variation between peak and slack loading which calls for trains to be uncoupled.

The 40 three-car units are equivalent to 100 of the older cars, each seating 64 on transverse seats and carrying a crush load of 355. The two end bodies are 13·31 m (43 ft 9 in) long with four double doors each side. The centre body is 10 m (32 ft 10 in) over couplings with three doors, each pair having a clear opening of 1·4 m (4 ft 7 in). The power is supplied by two pairs each of two nose-suspended motors of 92 h.p. on the central bogies.

Paris is pursuing a policy of renewing rolling stock in order to secure greater line capacity. Line 4 is the next to be dealt with, by providing rubber-tyred vehicles, and it is possible that they will become universal on the Metro by the end of this century. It is intended to deal with one line every four years, getting rid of all pre-1914 stock by 1975 and maintaining an average life of vehicles not exceeding 60 years.

Philadelphia

William Penn founded Philadelphia nearly 300 years ago, on the site of the present city centre, protected by the Delaware River to the south and east and the Schuylkill River to the west. By 1750 this was the second largest city in the English-speaking world, and for the next half-century it was considered to be the metropolis of America. A centennial exhibition in 1876 gave further impetus to its growth and the population is now almost 5 million. The city is intersected by two main arteries, Market Street from east to west and Broad Street running north and south. With few exceptions, north–south streets are numbered, Broad Street being in place of 14th Street, and the east–west Streets have names. Therefore, stations on the line running north and south are given street names, and on lines from east to west they are known by the street numbers.

The Philadelphia Transportation Company operate all metropolitan public transport, carrying some 550 million passengers a year, of which 140 million use the trains, which are underground in the centre and elevated in the suburbs. The route length of the system is $26\frac{3}{4}$ miles, which includes 18 miles of cut and cover tunnel and 43 underground stations. The booking halls are mostly sub-surface with steps to the platforms, and in many instances have direct entrances from buildings and shops as well as from the street. The two lines under Market Street and Broad Street cross at City Hall where a network of passages and concourses connect the underground stations, the Pennsylvania Railroad terminus and a number of office blocks and shops.

The Market Street Line is the oldest and carries the heaviest traffic, with 34 trains per hour in peak periods and a normal headway of 8 minutes. Construction started on April 6, 1903, and it was opened from 69th Street in the west to 15th Street in the city centre on March 4, 1907, and on to 2nd Street on August 3, 1908. Later in 1908 the line was taken south from 2nd Street along

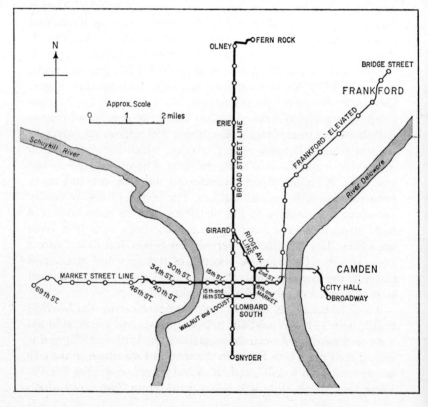

N

Approx. Scale
0   1   2 miles

FERN ROCK
OLNEY

BRIDGE STREET
FRANKFORD

Schuykill River

ERIE

BROAD STREET LINE

FRANKFORD ELEVATED

River Delaware

GIRARD

RIDGE AV. LINE

MARKET STREET LINE

34th ST.
30th ST.
15th ST.
2nd ST.

CAMDEN

69th ST.
46th ST.
40th ST.

15th and 16th ST.

8th and MARKET

CITY HALL
BROADWAY

WALNUT and LOCUST

LOMBARD SOUTH

SNYDER

PHILADELPHIA

Delaware Avenue, on the river bank, for about half a mile to South Street, but from May 8, 1939, this service was discontinued and all trains ran outwards over the Frankford Elevated. Up till November 1955 the line was elevated from 69th Street to a point just east of the Schuylkill River, whence it was underground; then, using an under-river tunnel constructed during the 1930 depression as a relief work, the line was taken underground from the city centre to the existing portal between 40th and 46th Street. An interesting feature of this double track line is the four-track tunnel between 32nd Street and City Hall, in which surface cars run parallel with the railway. The Frankford Elevated, which forms an extension to the Market Street Line from 2nd Street, was started on September 13, 1915, and opened on November 5, 1922. From the underground terminal at 69th Street to 2nd Street is 6·29 miles, of which 3·6 miles is in tunnel, and the Frankford Elevated runs for 6·51 miles from 2nd Street to Bridge Street.

The Broad Street Line was opened from Olney to City Hall on September 2, 1928, and extended to Lombard South on April 20, 1930, and to Snyder on September 18, 1938. On September 9, 1956, the existing underground tracks to a rolling-stock depot were utilized to take passengers on from Olney Avenue to the Fern Rock terminus. The tunnel between Olney and Walnut-Locust Station was built for four tracks but was only equipped with two except in the vicinity of Girard Station where connection was made with the Ridge Avenue Line. Four tracks were laid and operation of express trains between Erie and Walnut-Locust stations commenced on September 8, 1959. From Fern Rock to Snyder the tunnel is continuous for 8·62 miles.

The Ridge Avenue Line, opened on December 21, 1932, is 1½ miles long, from a junction with the Broad Street Line at Girard Station to the 8th and Market Street shopping centre, where there is interchange with the Market Street Line and the Locust Street–Camden Line. Since the Broad Street expresses were introduced in 1959 the Ridge Avenue Line trains run as locals as far as Erie Station.

The Locust Street–Camden Line was opened over 2·6 miles from Camden to 8th and Market Streets on June 7, 1936, and this section is owned by the Delaware River Port Authority. The extension to 16th and Locust Streets opened on February 15, 1953, adding 1·2 route miles. The line comes to the surface about half a mile west of the Delaware River which is crossed on the Benjamin Franklin Bridge and the last half-mile to the Broadway terminus in Camden is again underground.

Except where noted, all lines are double track and all are of normal 4 ft 8½ in gauge, except the Market Street Line which conforms to the 5 ft 2¼ in gauge of the elevated sections at both ends.

The permanent way is conventional with 100 lb/yd flat bottomed rail on timber sleepers, though there is a quantity of the old 90 lb/yd section rail not yet renewed on the Market Street Line. All lines work on 600 V d.c. from a 'dumb-bell' section third rail arranged for underside contact at 6 in above rail level. There is a maximum gradient of 1 in 20 and curvature down to 160 ft radius on the Broad Street and 105 ft radius on the Market Street Lines.

The signalling is by conventional, automatic block working with colour lights and trainstops.

The Broad Street Line has a fleet of 226 cars dating from before 1930, each 67 ft 6 in long with three sets of double doors on each side. Until recently the Market Street Line was operated with 315 even older cars built between 1906 and 1922, but these were replaced from 1960 onwards by 270 modern cars.

This modern car fleet consists of 46 cars which run as single units having driver's controls at both ends, and 224 designed to couple into pairs with a driving position at one end only. The single units seat 54 passengers and weigh 52,000 lb while the others seat 56 and weigh 50,000 lb. Trains can be built up from one to five couples of cars.

The seating is mainly transverse; there are six pairs of electropneumatically operated doors; pressure ventilation is provided and there is no paintwork in the interior. Each car measures 58 ft 4 in over couplings, 8 ft 1 in wide and 12 ft 9·5 in high.

Four 100 h.p. motors on each car drive the 28-in diameter wheels through right-angled hypoid gears giving a reduction of 8·14 : 1. The braking is rheostatic, which fades out below 4 m.p.h. and pneumatic brakes are provided for the final stop and for emergency. Acceleration up to 3 m.p.h. per second is provided with an ultimate top speed of 55 m.p.h. and braking is up to 2¾ m.p.h. per second. This gives an overall scheduled speed of 19 m.p.h. with 26 station stops in the 12 miles.

Cars now being delivered include 55 motor units to carry 27 passengers on transverse seats with 124 standing. These cars are built in stainless steel and have air suspensions. The control system includes dry silicon rectifiers and ignition phase control acceleration, and the maximum designed speed is 85 m.p.h.

In 1966 it is hoped to extend the Market Street service from Camden over the Pennsylvania Reading Seashore Line to New Jersey to serve Collingswood and Haddonfield and terminate at Kirkswood, 15 miles from Camden. A start was to be made in 1965 upon a 1½-mile extension southwards from Snyder. Further plans include the replacement of 6 miles of the Frankford Elevated by a new line partly underground, partly in cutting, and in part upon an elevated concrete structure with car parking space beneath.

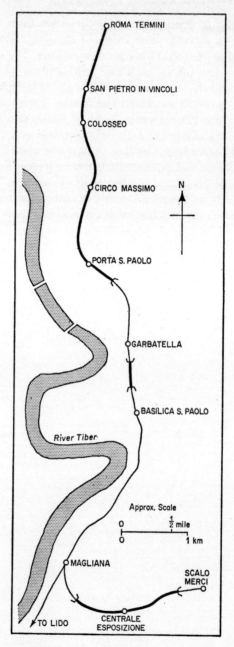

ROME

Rome

Rome was to be the centre of a World Fair in 1942, and in anticipation the Italian Government planned a line in 1938 to connect the main line terminus with the site of the Fair. Work on the main structures of the line was half completed when construction was halted in 1942. After the war, work was resumed on the badly damaged tunnels, in order to reduce unemployment. On February 9, 1955, operation of the line was started by a private company, the Societa Delle Tramvie e Ferrovie Electriche de Roma (STEFER).

Rome is the eternal city of the Seven Hills, but the line follows the valley of the Tiber River for most of its length of $11\frac{1}{3}$ km (7 miles). Starting about 150 ft above sea level beneath the main line terminus on St. Peter's Hill, it falls for $1\frac{1}{4}$ km (0·8 mile) at a gradient of about 1 in 30 and reaches its lowest point below the Pyramid of Caius Cestius near Porta San Paulo Station.

At San Paulo the suburban line connecting Rome and the Lido di Ostia starts and the underground comes to the surface to run parallel to the Lido Line as far as Magliana. At Magliana there is a connection to the Lido Line and some trains from the terminus turn off to Lido di Ostia, a distance of 25 km ($15\frac{1}{2}$ miles). From Magliano the line goes underground beneath the site for the World Fair to the two stations intended to serve it. This site has not yet been fully developed and consequently the line does not touch the more populated parts of the city and the traffic is not very intensive.

In general, the top of the tunnel is from 3 to 10 ft below street level, but climbing up to the terminus it is as much as 59 ft down. At the terminus end there are $3\frac{1}{2}$ km (2 miles) of double track tunnel and $\frac{1}{2}$ km ($\frac{1}{3}$ mile) in single tunnels which were mined through the rocky ground. At the south end $1\frac{1}{2}$ km (1 mile) of double track tunnel and about 0·2 km ($\frac{1}{8}$ mile) of single tunnels were built by cut and cover methods, and there are short tunnel sections at Porta san Paolo and Basilica di San Paolo. In all there are 6 km (3¾ miles) of tunnel. The double track tunnel is of elliptical shape 8 m (26 ft 3 in) wide and 5·5 m (18 ft) from rail level. Five of the ten stations are underground in elliptical enlargements of the tunnel with sub-surface booking halls. The stations have a naked appearance without decorative finishings, giving a massive architectural impression in keeping with the famous ancient monuments of the city, and are effectively lighted by lamps of the old-fashioned street-lamp shape.

The platforms are 4½ m (14 ft 9 in) wide and 156 m (512 ft) long, sufficient for eight-car trains, though the present traffic only justifies the use of two cars working at intervals of 6 minutes from Termini Station and 12 minutes beyond Magliana where some trains turn off to the Lido.

The track is of the standard 1·435 m (4 ft 8½ in) gauge with 46·5 kg/m (93 lb/yd) flat-bottomed rails spiked down upon timber sleepers embedded in ballast. The maximum gradient on the hill up to Termini Station is 1 in 28, but over the remainder of the line gradients do not exceed 1 in 85. Curvature is also easy the minimum radius being 200 m (656 ft). The distance between stations varies from 465 m (1525 ft) between Via Cavour and Colosseo, to 2296 m (7533 ft) between Basilica di San Paolo and Magliana.

The system works on 1500 V d.c. overhead lines, and is fed by four substations from the public supply.

Signalling is at present of the conventional automatic block type with track circuiting throughout, but consideration is being given to the installation of cab signalling suitable for 40 trains an hour.

The fleet of rolling stock comprises 40 motors and 8 trailers. The trailers are used only on the eight-car trains which run to the Lido, in the formation: motor, 2 trailers, 2 motors, 2 trailers, motor. Of the motors the first 18, which began trial running between Porta San Paolo and Espozione in May 1954, have two pantographs and two driving cabs. The other 22 of the more recent delivery have only one pantograph and one driving cab.

The first 18 seat 48 and the later cars have seating for 52 passengers on transverse seats and room for 195 standing at the official loading of 6 per square metre. Four pairs of electro-pneu-

matically operated doors on each side afford clear openings of
1¼ m (4 ft 1½ in).

The cars, built in Milan, have a length of 14·1 m (46 ft 3 in)
over end walls, are 3·04 m wide (9 ft 11½ in) and 3·61 m (11 ft
10 in) from rail level to roof. The exterior is painted light blue
picked out with a dark blue. The interior is well lighted by a
central continuous row of 40 fluorescent tubes working on 72 V
and is bright with a profusion of stainless steel posts and horizontal grip rails.

Each car is powered by four motors of 118 h.p. continuous
rating mounted longitudinally and driving the 0·9-m (35½ in)
wheels through a Cardan shaft and single bevel reduction gears.
The bogies have a trailing axle suspension with steel coil springs
acting in parallel with rubber. Acceleration is at 4½ km/hr (2·8
m.p.h.) per second initially and 3¼ km/hr (2 m.p.h.) per second up
to 40 km/hr (25 mp.h.). A maximum speed of 100 km/hr (62½
m.p.h.) is provided for use on the Lido Line where there are un-
interrupted runs of 5 or 10 km (3 or 6 miles).

Braking is rheostatic and compressed air with electromagnetic
rail brakes for emergency use. These are worked from the 72-V
battery equipment (also used for lighting) and are unusual in that
the shoe which grips the rail is composed of six separate sections,
jointed together and intended to take up any irregularities in the
track. The service rate of braking is 3 m.p.h. per second, of which
roughly half is provided by the rheostatic brakes.

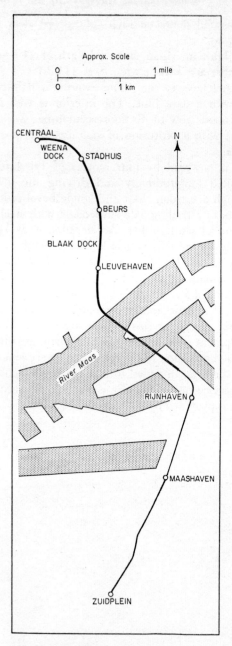

Approx. Scale

0 ———————————— 1 mile

0 ———————————— 1 km

CENTRAAL

WEENA DOCK

STADHUIS

N

BEURS

BLAAK DOCK

LEUVEHAVEN

River Maas

RIJNHAVEN

MAASHAVEN

ZUIDPLEIN

ROTTERDAM

Rotterdam

It is a curious fact that the city which is now the largest port in Europe, and one of the greatest in the world, was not on a river until 1572, when it was extended to the River Maas as a means of defence. It was not until 1872 that a direct deep-water connection to the North Sea initiated the city's growth as a port. The first docks were on the north bank, but later extensions were mainly on the south side of the river, and until recent years there was only one road bridge. Until this bridge was raised in 1926 it had to be opened even for the smallest ships and the tramway systems on both sides could not be connected.

Until 1942 this was the only road connection for the two halves of a city of $\frac{3}{4}$ million inhabitants, but in 1942 a vehicular tunnel was opened and rapidly became congested by a flow of up to 2800 vehicles an hour. In 1965 a high-level bridge with six lanes for fast traffic and one for cycles was opened to the east of the city centre across the island of Brienenoord. There are already delays of up to $\frac{1}{2}$ hour to traffic in the tunnel and on the tram lines which cross the approach roads. A tunnel connection on the Benelux Highway to the west of the city is expected to relieve congestion when opened in 1965, and the existing bridge is also to be replaced by a six-lane traffic tunnel but, largely because it involves the demolition of a thousand buildings, this is not scheduled for completion until 1970. Meanwhile the traffic has to wait for 20 minutes in every two hours while the bridge is opened for shipping.

The short underground railway now being constructed over $5\frac{3}{4}$ km ($3\frac{1}{2}$ miles) is expected to carry passengers at a rate of over 20,000 an hour in the evening peak period, from 5 to 5.15 p.m. The estimate of 250 million guilders compares favourably with the 150 million estimated cost of the six-lane tunnel with its expected capacity of only 3600 cars per hour in one direction. It is intended to run trains at $2\frac{1}{2}$ minute intervals initially and to increase the service up to $1\frac{1}{2}$ minute headway as it becomes necessary. The trains are to consist of three units of articulated stock, each unit seating 80 with a crowd load of 325 passengers.

South of the river, for roughly half its length, the line will be on a cantilevered viaduct of pre-stressed concrete carried by bored pile foundations. On the north side it will be underground.

The subsoil comprises 60 ft of peat and clay overlying sand, and is saturated with water up to 5 ft below street level. The Dutch engineers have defeated their ancient enemy, water, as they have so often done, by ingenious methods of making it serve them.

For the river crossing a huge dry dock was built on the isle of Brienenoord and within this complete sections of precast double track tunnel, 300 ft long and weighing 4500 tons, were constructed. Each section consisted of five or six portions joined by rubber inserts and pre-stressed together into a rigid unit for floating downriver to the site. The weight was accurately calculated to ensure that each section would float with only an inch or two above water, and the weight of the track would be sufficient to ensure against any tendency to float when the tunnel was equipped for service. On site the tunnel sections were positioned upon concrete piles which were fitted with cylindrical caps within which the head of the pile formed a piston. The accurate alignment of each section was made by pumping cement grout into this cylinder to force the cap upwards and to set hard as a firm foundation. Finally the sections were winched together under pressure, water was pumped out from between the steel bulkheads, and the pre-stress on each section was released. Thus a degree of flexibility was given by the rubber joints between each portion, a precaution thought necessary after the 1942 road tunnel had developed leaks caused by unequal settlement.

The central portion of the tunnel consists of about 200 m (650 ft) rising on a slight gradient towards Runhaven with rail level some 60 ft below the water level. This is approached by two sections also of about 200 m of 1 in 26 gradient.

The river crossing afforded an example of an existing technique in a highly developed form, but the adaptation of this to the construction of the tunnels under the streets in the city centre was truly original. The catastrophic bombing of Rotterdam in 1940 was used to advantage by providing two large bomb sites on the underground route suitable for the construction of the tunnel sections. Large dry docks were excavated to a depth of 12 m (39 ft) and floored with a 5½-m (18 ft) depth of firmly consolidated sand on which a concrete floor was laid. The tunnel segments were constructed in this dock, the ends being closed with thin concrete diaphragms, and when a batch was ready the dock was flooded.

Canals, 14 m (46 ft) wide and 11 m (36 ft) deep were dug between sheet piles from the entrance to the dock and along the line of the future tunnel and were allowed to fill with water. The tunnel segments were then floated into their final position, adjusted on piled foundations, and connected up just as was done beneath the river. The tunnel sections are from 60 to 70 m (197 to 230 ft) long with a centre wall between the two tracks, broken at intervals by access openings. For stations the length of a section is reduced to 50 m (164 ft) but the width is doubled to accommodate the platforms and reinforced concrete pillars between the tracks. The roofs of the tunnels are 5 m (16 ft 6 in) below street level, allowing room for sub-surface booking halls.

Traffic along the route of the canals was diverted, and trams stopped, but cross traffic, including trams, crossed the canal by temporary bridges. First the rectifier substation was constructed near to the Centraal Station, then the lengths of tunnel on either side of each dock, and in the summer of 1966 they will be connected across the dock sites. Work on the under-river section was finished in 1965 and the Brienenoord dock may now be used to build more sections for the land tunnels.

It was found possible to build Leuvehaven Station by the more conventional dry method and this is complete, while the other three underground stations are well advanced. The underground stations will have large booking halls under the street with stairs down to the platforms. Centraal Station will have an island platform 9 m (29 ft 6 in) wide but the other three are to have side platforms 3½ m (11 ft 6 in) wide and all platforms will be 120 m (394 ft) long to accommodate four articulated units.

The overhead section, south of the river, will have booking halls at ground level connected by escalators and stairs to the platforms above. Around Zuidplein, in the residential area of the city, the public street transport will be reorganized to focus upon the new station, which is to incorporate a two-level bus station and covered

M

parking for cycles. Work on this section started in 1964 and should be complete in 1966.

The rolling stock is being built in Holland and will consist of 27 articulated units of two bodies upon three bogies with a length over couplings of 29 m (95 ft 2 in) a width of 2·68 m (8 ft 10 in) and empty weight of 38,000 kg (37½ tons). Each unit will seat 80 passengers with 245 standing, at the crush loading of 7 passengers per square metre.

Six pairs of doors on each side give clear openings of 1·15 m (3 ft 9 in). There is a driving cab at both ends and all three bogies are powered by a pair of 110-h.p. motors driving all wheels through 8 to 49 hypoid gears. The acceleration will be at the rate of 2·9 km/hr (1·8 m.p.h.) per second and the maximum speed is to be 60 km/hr (37 m.p.h.) initially with provision for increasing this to 75 km/hr (46½ m.p.h.). Braking will be by a rheostatic system and by air giving a deceleration of 3·4 km/hr (2¼ m.p.h.) per second.

The fleet will be stabled and inspected in a surface depot to be built on land now owned by the National Railways, but the major overhauls and maintenance will be done at the Kleiweg depot of the Rotterdamse Elektrische Trams.

The system will have conventional track of the normal 4 ft 8½ in gauge and third rail equipment at 750 V d.c. but will share with Milan the distinction of rolling stock fitted with resilient wheels.

Visits were made to Toronto, New York and Cleveland to study modern signalling methods and the use of closed circuit television for station control. In these respects Rotterdam will be fully up to date and employing a minimum of staff and maximum automation.

Provision is made for extending northwards from Centraal Station and southwards from Zuidplein to new housing estates and at Beurs the station is already built as an interchange to a future east-west line with a tunnel crossing over the railway and used, temporarily, for the tramway service.

Stockholm

Stockholm is a city of close upon a million inhabitants, built upon rocky ground intersected by deep water channels which greatly obstruct the flow of surface traffic, and form difficult barriers to underground routes. In its seven centuries' life the city has been virtually rebuilt three times. About 1640 the narrow crooked alleyways were rebuilt as straight narrow streets, and after a great fire in 1751 the city was rebuilt to the same plan with the same narrow streets.

Replanning started in 1930 but it was not until 1951 that work started on a massive four-year rebuilding programme which was closely linked with the construction of an underground railway system. When the City Council decided, in 1941, to build this system, more than 60 schemes had already been examined and rejected in the previous 60 years, and even then a start was delayed, by the war, until 1945.

The system now comprises two lines. One in full operation from Hasselby in the west, through the centre of the city and to the south in three branches to Hagsatra, Farsta and Bagarmossen. The other, still under construction, will run from Ropsten in the east, parallel to the first line under the main waterway, and to the south-west in two branches to Varberg and Fruangen. It is now operating between Centralen, Ornsberg and Fruangen. It is expected that it will reach Ostermalmstorg and Bredang in May 1965, Satra in November 1965, Skarholmen in October 1966 and will be completed to Ropsten and Varberg by the end of 1967. The Farsta branch is to be extended by a kilometre to Farsta-Strand in 1967.

The route length of the first line is 40 km (25 miles) and of the 20 route km (12½ miles) of the second about 12½ km (8 miles) are in operation. Trains run at intervals of 2 minutes in the peak and 3 to 6 minutes in slack hours, with an overall speed of 31 km/hr (19½ m.p.h.) and, allowing for 30-second station stops, this gives a

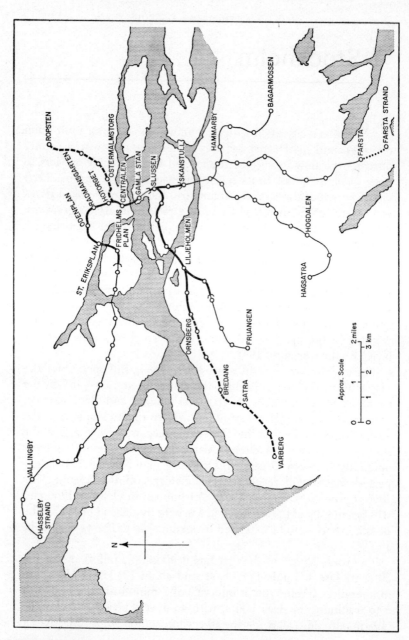

STOCKHOLM

line capacity of 36,000 passengers per hour per track. Over half a million passengers use the older line each day.

Of the 58 stations now open, 13 are completely underground and two are partly underground. The underground stations have sub-surface booking halls with entrances, wherever possible, from the adjacent buildings and access to the platforms by escalator. The underground station at Fridhelmsplan has a street-level booking hall at the western entrance, and at Skanstull the northern entrance booking hall is also on the surface.

The surface stations are built to a variety of plans with booking halls above, below, alongside the tracks, or even on the platform at unimportant stations. Where traffic is heavy or the difference in height between platform and street is considerable, escalators are provided at surface stations. The escalators are 1·2 m (4 ft) wide, at the normal angle of 30° and reversible, running at 39 m (128 ft) a minute for short flights, and 45 m (147 ft) a minute for long escalators. There are 77 escalators and 13 lifts.

Surface stations have under-floor heating, radiators on the walls, and heating coils in the steps from the street to clear away snow and ice. In many places this heating is by gas. Surface stations have fluorescent lighting to an intensity of 7 foot-candles, compared with up to 20 on underground platforms. Diesel-electric stand-by sets are installed at underground stations to provide emergency lighting to 4 foot-candles, and as a last resource there is a 24-V battery system to provide just sufficient light for slow movement.

Underground ticket hall and platform floors are of a cement mosaic containing sintered tiles or quartz, while the walls are finished with a great variety of interesting materials most artistically applied. Advertising is well controlled and restrained with posters of a few standard sizes in wooden frames, never simply pasted on the walls. Some halls and platforms are reserved for purely architectural decoration.

Platforms are 145 m (470 ft) long, mostly of the island type, 9 m (29 ft) wide in the central area, and 6 to 7 m (19 to 23 ft) in the outskirts. All platforms are connected to the central control office at Malartorget by a loudspeaker system, and a master clock controls all the platform clocks.

The surface soil of Stockholm consists of large areas of rock or moraine between which there is clay, especially in the western suburbs, and ridges of gravel, frequently surrounded by sand, run right across the city and along the shore at Gamla. In places the soil is very corrosive to iron and steel. The underlying rock is gneiss and granite with local inclusions of greenstone and is intersected by fault planes and moraine-filled valleys with rotten rock which is liable to flow.

Rock tunnels have been built where possible, although this means keeping at a considerable depth, but several interesting tunnelling methods have been used to meet various soil conditions, and a brief description of the variation in the tunnels of the first line will illustrate this.

The line from the west leaves the surface by a short concrete tunnel leading into a rock tunnel, which soon splits into two tunnels approaching Fridhelmsplan. The station has shallow cover and is in unsound rock which has required reinforcement for the two platform tunnels, $5\frac{1}{2}$ m (about 18 ft) wide.

A 1 in 25 grade through rock and concrete tunnels rises to the St. Erik bridge where the line is suspended below the roadway. A short concrete tunnel leads to St. Eriksplan station which was built by cut and cover methods as a two-pin frame round an island platform, because it is in a water bearing infilling of quarry rubbish.

Rock tunnel leads on to Odenplan, a station cut out of the rock as an arched tunnel 15·3 m (50 ft) wide and 5·67 m (18 ft 6 in) high from the island platform. There follows a concrete tunnel through gravel beneath important buildings which had to be underpinned. Then Radmansgarten is reached, on the edge of a gravel ridge with alternate steeply slanting layers of sand and clay. It was found impossible to drive piles and the station consists of a reinforced concrete box with wedge-shaped expansion joints to allow for ground movement, and provision has been made for possible jacking-up of the upper part if the heavy concrete invert sinks.

The next section is on a layer of clay up to 8 m deep, which would not support a tunnel without piling. To avoid damage to surrounding buildings the tunnel was built by cut and cover methods and then jacked up by piles driven through holes in the roof and invert by a pile driver standing on the tunnel roof.

Hotorget, the next station, is a steel-framed structure with a

172

sub-surface booking hall over the tracks partitioned off with glass from broad pedestrian passages giving access to shops and the street.

Up to Centralen station there are twin concrete box tunnels and part of this station, beneath Klara churchyard, is built as a rock tunnel with very thin cover and is reinforced by pre-stressed reinforced concrete arched ribs. This tunnel contains four tracks, for the older line is here joined by the newer one.

Here there is cross platform interchange between trains running in opposite directions. Trains from Hasselby and to Ostermalm-strog will arrive at one platform and on another level trains to Hasselby will share a platform with those from Ostermalmstrog. This is one of the two busiest stations (Hotorget is the other) and there is a direct pedestrian connection to the Central main line station.

We now come to the 1 in 25 approach to the crossing under the Norrstrom where the four tracks are at the same level. The rock surface in this section is very irregular and the ground above is very difficult, necessitating chemical freezing of the soil and working in compressed air caissons.

The Gamla station has a subsurface booking hall, tracks at ground level, and a road viaduct over them. Every year the ground suffers both vertical and horizontal movement and the booking hall, below ground water level, has expansion joints designed to accommodate up to 10 in movement and sealed by a heavily corrugated copper diaphragm sandwiched between flexible plastic (polyisobutylene).

The line crosses the Soderstrom on a five-track bridge, the fifth track being a siding, and runs on a concrete viaduct to Slussen, a station which is partly blasted out of solid rock. About 100 m beyond Slussen the two routes divide.

The tunnels are ventilated by reversible fans between stations, with relief shafts at both ends of the stations. The fan shafts have a 16m² cross section with an average of three fans in each, giving a capacity of 200,000m³ per hour.

The track gauge is 1·435 m (4 ft 8½ in). The 50 kg/m (101 lb/yd) and 43·2 kg/m (87 lb/yd) rails are 20 m long welded into lengths of up to 250 m (820 ft) with eight-hole blockjoint fishplates. They are laid on rubber pads and steel baseplates secured by four elastic spikes to timber sleepers at 65 cm (2 ft 1½ in) spacing in ballast. Old sleepers were of Swedish pine treated with arsenic or creosote, but now creosote-impregnated beech is used. They are of 16 × 22 cm (6¼ × 8¾ in) cross section 2·6 m (8 ft 6 in) long with every fourth sleeper 2·8 m (9 ft) long to carry the conductor rail. There is an experimental length of track upon longitudinal concrete bearers and concrete sleepers are being tested in the track.

The third rail is of low carbon steel, flat-bottomed with an unusually heavy web and foot, weighing 60 kg/m (121 lb/yd), 15 m (49 ft) long welded into lengths up to 300 m (328 yd) and anchored at the centre. There is top contact with a protection board mounted 75 mm (3 in) above the rail upon brackets fixed to the sleepers. The heavy falls of dry snow, which drifts in the winter, tends to become packed on top of the rail by the passing shoes and to form a very effective insulator. Special cars are run on the open sections to blow away the snow, using air forced through nozzles at conductor rail level by a centrifugal fan driven by a 65-h.p. motor. In addition the current rails can be heated in non-traffic hours by passing traction current through short-circuited sections.

The 700-V d.c. traction current is taken through 31 rectifier substations from the 30-kV supply of the Northern Swedish Water Power stations by a special double cable system with no other load connected to it. Normally each cable supplies alternate substations, but each cable can supply any substation in an emergency.

Substations in the city centre have been blasted out of solid rock. They are not normally manned but are controlled from a central point. The standard size is 3000 kW (four 750 kW rectifiers) but at Klara and Munkbron, which feed two routes, there are two 3000 kW equipments at each. Four mobile 1500 kW convertor stations are available for emergencies.

The signalling system is of particular interest as the first application of cab signalling in Europe or upon any underground system. The only fixed signals are those at junctions, but a small three aspect signal in the cab gives a continuous indication to the driver. The three aspects are H, permitting speeds up to 70 km/hr (44 m.p.h.), M up to 50 km/hr (31 m.p.h.) and L restricting speed to 15 km/hr (9½ m.p.h.) It is proposed to increase the maximum to 80 km/hr (49½ m.p.h.).

The cab signal is operated by impulses picked up through two receiver coils by induction from the running rails, which are divided into sections by blockjoints, with impedance bonds to pass the return traction current. The track sections are energized with 75 c/s a.c. current which is coded at 180 impulses a minute for the H indication, 75 for M and no impulses for L. If the driver does not react correctly to the signal within 1½ seconds, the emergency brakes are automatically applied.

The fixed signals which protect the automatically operated points have a Green aspect for proceeding in accordance with the cab signal, Red for stop and wait, and Red/Yellow for stop and proceed under caution. The route indicator consists of two or three green lights. Routes are set up and the points and fixed signals are remotely controlled from two signal towers at Gullsmarsplan and at Alvik, where 15 km of double track is indicated on a diagram 10 m long.

The fleet of 600 cars are of four types, all painted green. The older cars all seat 48 passengers with from 90 to 108 standing, and weigh 28·2 or 30·1 tons. The newer 150 cars weigh only 23·6 tons and seat 48 with 108 standing. The seating is lateral with three pairs of double doors on each side, giving an opening of 1·2 m (3 ft 11 in). All the cars are 17·4 m (56 ft 6 in) over couplings, 2·8 m (9 ft 2 in) over the waist, and from rail to roof 3·72 m (12 ft 1 in).

The side windows can be lowered 200 mm (8 in) for ventilation, and heating is from 35 kW auxiliary heaters and fans, between the ceiling and the roof, blowing warm air through perforations in the roof and openings at the windows and under the seats. Waste heat is not used, the auxiliary heaters giving a more accurate and complete control. Lighting is by cold cathode fluorescent tubes giving 10 foot-candles at one metre above the floor, and emergency lighting is provided by six 15-W lamps.

The car bodies are of all steel construction with walls, roof, and underframe included in the load-carrying structure. The underframe and the floor are of welded steel, the side walls are of 1·5 mm steel reinforced by corrugated plates of the same thickness spot welded inside.

The all-welded bogies have no conventional bolster, swing links or leaf springs. The journal boxes are rubber mounted on the side beams and house large spherical roller bearings. The side beams are held by vertical coil springs below an H-beam which, in turn, is held by coil springs to a swivelling box-section beam that pivots upon a centre pin.

Each bogie carries two motors rated at 115 h.p. at 700 V, fully sprung and driving the 0·864-m (34 in) diameter wheels through a universal jointed shaft and single reduction gearing of 1 : 7·235 ratio, mounted on the axles. This gives an initial acceleration of 3·6 km/hr (2¼ m.p.h.) per second. Rheostatic braking is used down to 6 km/hr where electro-pneumatic brakes take over and emergency braking is by Westinghouse type air brakes. The average retardation in service is 4 km/hr (2½ m.p.h.) per second. Eight experimental cars of a particularly light design (Type C 5) were ordered in 1959 and should be under test before this book is published.

There are four maintenance depots, at Spanga near Vallingby (208 car capacity), Hogdalen (192), Hammarby (64) and the newest at Nybodahallen (214). Nybodahallen was opened in 1964 and includes a bus garage in which 30 railway cars are stabled on four tracks, and another 64 cars are housed on four tracks in two rock tunnels about 300 m long. The remaining cars are stored, 24 on three tracks of the maintenance shed, and 96 on six tracks in a new protected area. At Hammarby, also, half the depot is given over to buses and trolleybuses. Cleaning inside and outside, brake and cab signal checking and general inspection takes place every second day, and there is a complete inspection over a pit every 6000 km (3728 miles). Wheels are reground after 200,000 km (124,000 miles) and at 400,000 km (250,000 miles) cars have a complete overhaul, being stripped down to a skeleton and renewed as necessary.

Automatic driving is being tested on a system based on the cab signalling equipment. Instead of operating visual signals the impulses from the rails are fed into apparatus which compares the train speed with the required speed and initiates acceleration or braking as appropriate. The intention is to replace the present driver and guard by one man who will supervise from the cab and operate the doors.

Tokyo

The industrial development of Japan has been phenomenal in the last 20 years, and the capital city increased in population by more than 50 per cent between 1950 and 1960. The central area of Tokyo has grown upwards in large multi-storey buildings, though the ground is not really suitable for sky-scrapers. There is now a population of over $8\frac{1}{2}$ million in the 560 km² (220 square miles) under the control of the Metropolitan Government, and the whole city covers an area of 2027 km² (783 square miles) with a population comparable with that of Greater London, some $10\frac{1}{2}$ million inhabitants.

The suburbs are still expanding rapidly and the ownership of private car transport is progressing towards an American standard. Already the traffic congestion is comparable with that in London, and a cure for the threatening paralysis of the commuter traffic is being sought with great urgency and very great expense in the construction of new highways, road widening and flyovers, but chiefly in the building of underground railways.

The Japanese National Railways carry about a third of the commuter traffic on the Yamate loop line which encircles the city centre, the Chuo Line which is the only main line through the city, and on the five main lines which radiate from the Yamate loop, but there are no main line termini within the loop. The congestion on the loop is increased by the fact that fourteen privately owned lines radiate from termini which are served by the Yamate loop, bringing in another quarter of the total traffic.

The J.N.R. and some of the private lines operate on a narrower than standard track gauge, and the programme of underground construction provides for through running over some of these, which also have different systems of electrification. The underground system of Tokyo is therefore unique in the variety of its equipment. The two self-contained lines, the Ginza and Maranouchi lines, Lines 3 and 4, have standard gauges (1·435 m or

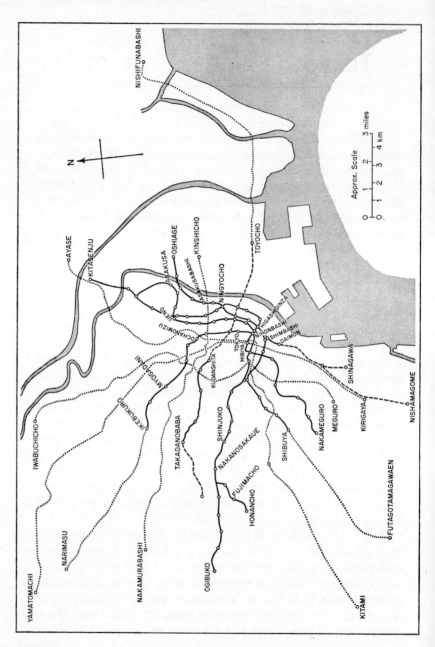

NISHIFUNABASHI

N

Approx. Scale

3 miles

4 km

3

2

1

0

AYASE

KITASENJU

OSHIAGE

ASAKUSA

KINSHICHO

ASAKUSABASHI

NINGYOCHO

TOYOCHO

UENO

OCHANOMIZU

IZUMIZU

HIGASHIGINZA

NIHONBASHI

SHIMBASHI

DAIMON

TOYOKO

KUDANSHITA

HIBIYA

SHINAGAWA

MYOGADANI

IKEBUKURO

SHINJUKO

NAKAMEGURO

SHINAGAWA

KIRIGAYA

NISHIMAGOME

IWABUCHICHO

TAKADANOBABA

NAKANOSAKAUE

SHIBUYA

MEGURO

NARIMASU

FUJIMACHO

HONANCHO

NAKAMURABASHI

OGIBUKO

FUTAGOTAMAGAWAEN

YAMATOMACHI

KITAMI

TOKYO

4 ft 8½ in) and a third rail for current. The Oshiage Line, Line 1, is also of standard gauge but has an overhead wire current system, while the Hibiya Line, Line 2, is on a narrow gauge track with overhead wiring and the Tozai Line, Line 5, is constructed to the same standards.

Because of these fundamentally different standards, it is convenient to describe each line separately.

Line 1, the Oshiage Line, is owned and worked by the transportation bureau of the Tokyo Metropolitan Government. It is in operation between Oshiage in the east and Daimon on the southern fringe of the central area, a distance of 8·9 km (5½ miles). Work is in hand on a further 3·4 km (2 miles) to Shinagawa and this section should be in service during 1966. Construction of this line was started in 1958 and in 1960 the first 3·2 km (2 miles) from Oshiage to Asakusabashi was opened, a further 0·6 km (0·4 mile) was completed to Higashi Nihonbashi at the end of May 1962, another 1 km (0·6 miles) to Ningyocho at the end of September 1962, the next 2·6 km (1·6 miles) to Higashi Ginza on February 28, 1963, and the remainder to Daimon in late 1963 and 1964.

This Oshiage Line is of standard track gauge (1·435 m or 4 ft 8½ in) with an overhead current supply of 1500 V d.c. in a double track, box-type tunnel. The signalling is of the automatic block type with three aspect colour light and trainstops. The traffic is carried in four-car trains with a 3-minute interval in the rush-hour and 5 minutes in off peak, the overall scheduled speed being 28·2 km/hr (17½ m.p.h.). About 31 million passengers use this line every year for journeys averaging 3·6 km (2¼ miles).

The other three lines are the responsibility of the Teito Rapid Transport Authority, an organization established on July 4th, 1941, to take over the Tokyo Underground Railway Company, the Keihin Underground Railway, the Teito Rapid Transit Company, and the Tokyo City Underground lines. The Authority is under the supervision of a cabinet minister who is responsible for appointing the members of its board. The T.R.T.A. is authorized to issue public bonds up to ten times the amount of its capital and can obtain government loans and subsidies. There is therefore no difficulty in financing the great extension of its system which has been planned for completion in 1966.

The longest line of the T.R.T.A. is the Maranouchi Line, Line 4, which runs from Ogikubo eastwards to the city with a branch 2·7 km (1·7 miles) long to Honancho from Honcho Dori. Passing under the city from Nishiginza in the south to Ochanomizo in the north, it again turns west to Ikebukuro, making a total route length of 27·4 km (17 miles) and it is planned to carry the line on to Narimasu, a further 8 km (5 miles) at some future date.

The Maranouchi Line carries 267 million passengers a year, more than any of the other lines of the system, and the average length of passenger journey, 6·4 km (4 miles), is the longest.

At Ogikubo there is interchange with the Japanese National Railways Chuo Line and the Hunancho branch serves a district without any other rapid railway service to the city. It is at Fujimicho on this branch that the main rolling-stock depot and works are located. The line passes through residential districts to Shinjuku where two of the radial private railways terminate, and the interchange to the J.N.R. Yamate loop line and Chuo line produces heavy traffic.

Six-car trains run throughout the main line and only two-car trains on the branch. On the main line from Maranouchi round to Shinjuko the train intervals are 2 minutes for the peak and 4 minutes for off peak periods. At Shinjuku alternate trains are reversed and the intervals become 4 and 8 minutes to Ogibuko and to Honancho. The scheduled speed is 26·8 km/h (16¾ m.p.h.) from Maranouchi to Shinjuku, 34·2 km/h (21½ m.p.h.) to Ogibuko and 27·4 km/h (17 m.p.h.) on the branch.

The line is of standard gauge in double track rectangular tunnels, having a clearance gauge 7·8 m (25 ft) wide and 3·9 m (12 ft 9 in) from rail level, with central supports. The signalling is automatic block, three aspect colour light with trainstops. The rolling stock is maintained at Fujimicho on the Honancho branch and the Koishikawa depot and works near Myogadani, the second station from Ikebukuro. The 312 cars are 18 m (59 ft) long by 2·79 m (9 ft 2 in) wide and 3·495 m (11 ft 6 in) from rail level, weighing 34½ tons. They are straight sided with three double doors on each side, painted red with a distinctive wide white band at waist level and designed to carry 150 passengers, of which 54 can be seated.

Braking is by a combination of the rheostatic and electro-pneumatic systems, and each coach has four motors taking 300 V d.c. from a third rail fed by eleven substations.

Construction of the section between Ikebukuro and Tokyo main line station was started in 1951 and the line was opened in stages up to July 1956. Tokyo to Shinjuku was started upon in 1956 and opened throughout in March 1959. The remainder of the line, from Shinjuku to Ogibuku and Honancho was started in March 1959 and opened in sections up to March 1962. This section beyond Shinjuku is often referred to as the Ogikubo Line, as distinct from the remainder which is the Maranouchi Line proper.

The Ginza Line, Line 3, is the second longest with a route length of 14·3 km (9 miles), of which all but 0·4 km is in tunnel, and is also the oldest of Tokyo underground lines, having been constructed between 1925 and 1939. The northern portion, Asakusa to Shimbashi (8 km), was built by the Tokyo Underground Railway Company and completed in June 1934. The first section of 2·2 km (1·4 miles) between Asakusa and Ueno is the earliest length of underground railway in the east, having been opened in 1927. The southern portion between Shimbashi and Shibuya (6·3 km) was built by the Tokyo Rapid Transit Company, opened in January 1938, and used for through running from Asakusa in September 1939. The speed of construction of this line averaged only 1 km a year, owing to difficulties of finance experienced by these private companies. The advantage of the state controlled T.R.T.A. and the advances in technique are illustrated by the building of more recent underground lines at an average rate of 8½ km a year through ground offering the same or greater engineering difficulties.

The Ginza Line starts from the Shibuya station of the Japanese National Railways in the south, where three of the radial privately owned railways terminate.

Extensions have recently been opened northwards from Asakusa for about 2 km to Minowa and South West from Shibuya for some 10 km to Futagotamagawaen closely following the Tokyo–Tamagawa privately owned line.

The Ginza Line does not inter-run with any other line and has therefore been free to choose the standard track gauge of 1·435 m (4 ft 8½ in) and a third rail system of 300 V d.c. fed from six substations. The tunnels are of rectangular section with central pillars between the two tracks, and a clear width of 7·64 m (26 ft 3 in) and a height of 3·73 m (12 ft 3 in) above rail level.

Signalling is the same as on the Maranouchi Line with three aspect colour lights and trainstops. On both lines speed control is used at terminal station approaches and on severe down gradients.

The rolling stock consists of 21 cars each powered by four motors and weighing 29½ tons. They are 16 m (52 ft 6 in) long 2·5 m (8 ft 2½ in) wide and 3·5 m (11 ft 6 in) high. They carry 44 seated passengers with 81 standing and appear very similar to the Maranouchi Line cars except that they are painted a light tan colour without external decoration or lettering other than the car number.

In the morning peak, six-car trains are run at two-minute intervals, at midday five cars at three minutes, and for the evening peak five cars at a 2½-minute headway, at a scheduled speed of 24·9 km/hr (15·6 m.p.h.).

Traffic is as heavy as on the Maranouchi Line with a total of over 200 million passengers a year making journeys of an average length of 4·8 km (3 miles).

The Hibiya Line, Line 2, is the most modern, the section from Kita Senju to Higashi Ginza 11·7 km (7·4 miles) long, having been built between early 1959 and late 1962. A second section from Higashi Ginza to Naka Meguro 8·7 km (5·4 miles) was completed in August 1964.

The line runs southwards from Kita Senju, a factory area to the north of the city, where a connection for through running is made with the privately owned Tobu railway, through the city centre and out to Naka Meguro in the south-western suburbs, where it again connects to inter-run upon the Tokyo Kyuko Electric Railways Line.

Because of this through running over other railways, the track gauge is 1·067 m (3 ft 6 in) and the current is supplied from overhead wires at 1500 V d.c. from three substations.

The signalling is of the normal automatic block type with three aspect colour lights but employing a system of automatic train control in place of the more conventional mechanical trainstop. This is a continuous induction system with audio frequency track circuits giving a continuous control of train speed within specified limits over any track section. Within this range there is no interference with the driver's control of his train but a transistorized unit in his cab takes control if the speed is too high or too low until it has brought the speed back within the correct range. The emergency brake is automatically applied when a de-energized track circuit is entered, or on failure of the signal current.

From September 1964, a system of automatic train operation has been in service over the 6·2 km (4 miles) section between Minami Senju and Ningyocho and the six intermediate stations. This apparatus is based upon the automatic train control mentioned above which came into use in March 1961, but it goes a stage further, removing the control from the driver's hands.

The speed of the train is controlled, after the driver has pressed a button to start, by comparison of the train speed as indicated by a generator on the axle, with the correct speed as indicated by the pulse rate of the track circuit which varies with the aspect of the appropriate signal.

The driver is in constant communication with the traffic controller and substation attendant by means of radio telephony.

The 202 cars are of stainless steel and outwardly very similar to those of the other T.R.T.A. lines, but they are unpainted and, being longitudinally corrugated both below and above a plain section containing the windows, have a pleasing, functional appearance. The pneumatic bogie suspension has proved very satisfactory and quieter than the conventional metal springing of the other lines.

Four motors of 100 h.p. give a maximum speed of 100 km/hr (62·2 m.p.h.) and acceleration of 4 km/hr (2½ m.p.h.) per second. The cars weigh 32 tons, are 18 m (59 ft) over couplings, 2·79 m (9 ft 2 in) wide and 3·6 m (11 ft 10 in) from rail level to roof. They seat 52 passengers, have a crush capacity of 140, or 150 in the more modern type, and have electric heating, fan ventilation and fluorescent lighting.

The cars are all motors fitted with single pantographs, and in the tunnel section, running over T.R.T.A. lines, space has been saved by using a T-shaped overhead bar in place of the normal catinary wire. An extruded aluminium T-section bar, 8 × 12 cm (3⅛ × 4¾ in), has a grooved hard-drawn copper wire attached to the bottom of the vertical leg. Expansion joints are provided at 200 m intervals and between these the bar is anchored in such a way as to wander from side to side of the centre line over a distance of 20 cm (7¾ in) in order to spread the wear upon the pantograph.

Four- or six-car trains are used at 3-minute intervals in the morning and evening rush-hours and at 4-minute intervals at midday. The scheduled speed is 28·3 km/h (17½ m.p.h.). The line is used by 62 million passengers a year making an average journey of 4·8 km (3 miles).

The track in all the tunnel sections has a flat concrete invert with a deep central drainage channel and no transverse sleepers. The 50 kg/m (101 lb/yd) rails are laid on rubber pads which bear directly upon reinforced concrete blocks grouted into the mass concrete of the invert.

On straight track and large radius curves the rail is held down by shaped rubber blocks 15 cm (0·6 in) thick which are trapped and restrained from expansion upwards or outwards by four steel angle clips. These clips are anchored through the precast blocks into the mass concrete invert by ragbolts and secured by volute spring washers and nuts. Thus the rail does not make contact with steel or concrete except through the insulation provided by the rubber. This reduces vibration and noise as well as insulating the track circuits. Additional electrical insulation is given by the holding down bolts being covered with polyethylene.

On sharper curves the thickness of the pad beneath the rail is reduced to 12 cm (½ in) and the rail is secured by direct contact with steel spring clips. The holding-down bolts are embedded only in the reinforced concrete blocks and are insulated from the concrete by a nylon coating. The heel of the spring clip bears upon a steel insert in a nylon pad.

With both these somewhat flexible fastenings the rails are held against outwards movement, or gauge widening, by thrust blocks bearing upon the outside of the web of the rail.

The first section of a new Line, the Tozai Line, or Line 5, was opened on December 23, 1964, for 4·8 km (3 miles) between Taka-danobaba and Kudanshita. Work is now in progress to extend this to Nakano 4·1 km to the west, and Toyocho 7·1 km to the east, to give a line 16 km (10 miles) long. This is a 1·067 m (3 ft 6 in) gauge line working from an overhead wire on 1500 V.

The 18 cars are all 20 m (65 ft 8 in) long, 2·87 m (9 ft 5 in) wide

184

and 3·775 m (12 ft 5 in) high. The motors weigh 36 tons and the trailers 27½ tons. They run as three-car trains in the form control trailer, motor, control motor, at five-minute intervals, and an overall speed of 27·4 km/hr (17 m.p.h.). The control cars seat 50 and the motors without driving controls seat 58, and there is room for 86 passengers standing in every car. The usual heating and ventilation is provided with air ducts below the longitudinal seats and fans in the roof. The exterior is finished in aluminium with a blue waist rail.

All the underground lines in Tokyo, both existing and proposed, are shallow sub-surface lines because of the geology of the district. The surface of the central area consists of an alluvial deposit up to 30 m (98 ft) in depth and is very soft and wet. The suburbs, farther inland, are built on higher ground of an undulating character consisting of a layer of 15 to 25 ft of volcanic ash over confused strata of clay, sand and sandstone. The difference in the average level of the suburban and central areas is as much as 50 m (164 ft) and a tube railway could not be built under either district at a reasonable and convenient depth without great expense being incurred in combating the difficult soil conditions.

The variety of engineering technique employed in constructing the Tokyo underground through such difficult ground is exceptional, and worthy of illustration by a few examples of particular works.

At Shinjuko the sub-surface station was constructed directly beneath ten tracks of the J.N.R. without disturbance of the main line traffic by the normal cut and cover method. This involved excavating and casting the tunnel walls *in situ*, underpinning the tracks and constructing the roof before completing the excavation and forming the invert.

For Hibiya station the excavation was to a depth of 22½ m (74 ft) below the street to contain the station tunnels at low level, a pedestrian concourse for the full width of 18·9 m (62 ft) above this, and an underground four-lane motorway superimposed on the concourse. The site is where there was an inlet of Tokyo Bay some 300 years ago, and the soil is a very soft deposit of silty clay containing quantities of water, and the street above carries very heavy motor cars and tramway traffic.

A row of sheet piling was driven on each side of the street which was replaced by a heavy timber deck and the first 7 m (23 ft) of excavation was completed by normal cut and cover methods. In the space thus provided a caisson was built and sunk step by step. Each caisson is about 12 m (39 ft 4 in) long and six were sunk at intervals along the 152-m (500 ft) length of the station. In order to save time, these were spaced out at intervals and the intervening spaces were excavated by normal cut and cover methods using the support provided by the caissons.

The Icos process was used in appropriate conditions. A brief description of this is given in the section dealing with Milan Underground.

For tunnelling at a greater depth in bad ground a shield has been used, notably near the National Diet building where the tunnels pass through water bearing sand with a cover of more than 15 m (49 ft) and near Toyocho on the new Tozai Line, Line 5.

Lines 6, 7, 8 and 9 have been proposed and planning is in progress. Line 6 runs from north-west to south between Yamatomachi and Kirigaya on Line 1, a distance of 30½ km (19 miles). Line 7 is directly north to south from Iwabuchicho to Meguro, 20¼ km (12¾ miles). Line 8 runs parallel to the Tozai Line, Line 5, but just north of it between Nakamurbashi and Kinsicho, 17½ km (11 miles) and finally Line 9 is from north-east to south-west for 32½ km (20 miles) between Ayaze and Kitami. When all these lines are in service, the system will have a route length of nearly 220 km (137 miles).

Toronto

Toronto is a young city based upon a large natural harbour on Lake Ontario. Until 1921 its development was hindered by a 30-year grant of exclusive rights to private operators of public transport within the narrow city boundaries of 1891. These operators refused to expand their system and in 1911 the city provided additional services within the modern boundary but they could not enter the central area, and consequently there were nine separated disjointed systems by 1920. On September 1, 1921, the newly formed Toronto Transportation Commission took over the operation of all public transport within the 35 square miles of the city and soon started to construct an underground railway. This body was succeeded in 1954 by the Toronto Transit Commission, responsible for all services within the city and 12 suburban municipalities, serving 240 square miles and 1¾ million people.

Canada's first underground railway, the Yonge Street Line, was opened on March 30, 1954. It starts from an underground terminus at Eglington Avenue and runs in open cutting southwards for 1½ miles before going into cut and cover tunnel for another three miles to Union Station. On February 28, 1963, the University Line was opened, extending the Yonge Street Line from Union Station back up University Avenue to St. George Station on Bloor Street.

The existing system consists only of 6½ miles of very modern line, but work is proceeding rapidly upon a further 8 miles from east to west beneath Bloor Street and along Danforth Avenue. Work started in 1962, already much of the track has been laid, and the whole is scheduled for completion early in 1966. A further extension of 3 miles at each end has been approved and is expected to be completed by the end of 1967. The route length of the system will then be 21 miles.

The Yonge Street Line carries about 75 million passengers a year, the University Line 8½ million, and it is expected that the

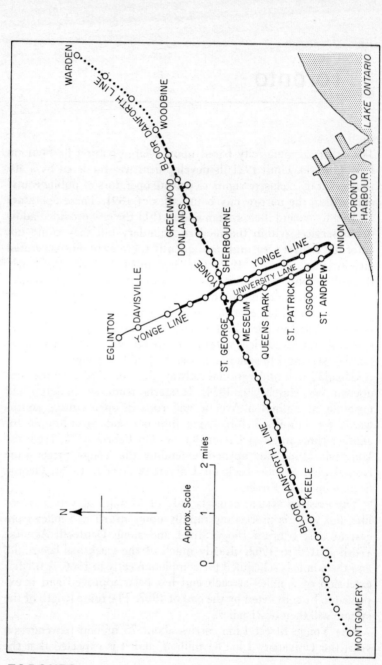

TORONTO

Bloor–Danforth Line will carry over 100 million. In the rush-hour 12,000 passengers per hour use Yonge Station and 9,000 of these come from street cars which will be displaced by the new underground line. The present service is of 27 trains per hour, each composed of four cars in the slack hours and eight in the peak, and the line is designed for a maximum of 40,000 passengers an hour in each direction.

The 18 stations of the Yonge Street and University Lines are of shallow construction except for St. Patrick and Queen's Park, which are of tube type. All the University Line stations have escalators and sub-surface booking halls. The cut and cover stations of the University Line are all similar in design to Union and Eglington on the Yonge Street Line, but three different wall finishes have been used in order to test the durability and cost of maintenance. At Osgoode and St Andrew, glass-faced masonry, similar to the Yonge Street stations; at Museum and Queen's Park large, glazed, ceramic tiles (16 × 8 in); and at the tube stations porcelain enamelled steel panels to fit the curved walls. There are suspended ceilings at the tube stations and all ceilings are treated with acoustic plaster. The lower portions of the tunnel walls and the platform walls, have been sprayed with ¾ in of asbestos to deaden noise.

The University Line is in cut and cover, except between Osgoode Street and the north end of Queen's Park where it was advisable to use tube tunnel construction because of the depth of the line, the necessity of avoiding noise and disturbance to the Hospital and other important buildings, and the prospect of underpinning the Provincial Parliament buildings. This tube section is as much as 30 ft below the street, but the normal depth of the cut and cover tunnels is such as to provide about 8 ft of cover to obviate damage from the severe frosts to which Toronto is subject.

In constructing the tube section it was not possible to use mechanized digger shields because of the loose ground containing large boulders, but the Greathead shields were highly developed and self-contained, the only services connected to them being electric cables. The silt and sand was very wet as well as loose, so that it was necessary to tunnel in 10 to 20 lb/in² of compressed air, and grouted and caulked cast iron linings were used as on the original London tubes. The 16 ft diameter running tunnels were driven by four shields, 17 ft 6 in external diameter and weighing 70 tons each. The 24 ft diameter station tunnels were driven by two 25 ft 9 in external diameter shields of 130 tons weight.

The Milan method was used experimentally for a short section of 162 ft to the east of St. George Station to minimize traffic disturbance where the line crosses under Bloor Street. In the earlier construction work under Yonge Street, temporary decking was necessary and this caused very serious traffic difficulties.

The cut and cover tunnels of the Yonge Street Line are formed of reinforced concrete frames 32 ft 6 in wide and 17 ft 8 in high. At stations the tunnel is 52 ft 4 in wide to allow for two side platforms of 12 ft width or island platforms 24 ft wide at termini. On the University Line the tunnels are 33 ft 2 in wide and 17 ft 8 in deep, divided into two sections each 13 ft 6 in wide and 13 ft 0 in from rail level, and the station tunnels are 59 ft wide. For noise reduction, the lowest 16 in of the running tunnel walls and the space below the platform nosings of stations is lined with a rockwool blanket $\frac{3}{4}$ in thick. All the platforms are 500 ft long throughout the system but on the newer lines island platforms are standard and the width has been increased to 29 ft 6 in.

The intensity of lighting in all public areas is $7\frac{1}{2}$ to 10 foot-candles, by fluorescent tubes 4 ft long with alternate tubes on a separate circuit, and emergency lighting is provided at all stations with a capacity of 10 to 14 kW for three hours fed with d.c. from batteries.

The present terminal station at St. George is a shallow station designed to be converted to a two-level layout when the Bloor–Danforth station has been built below the existing works. The junction will be to the west of the station and the trains diverging from Bloor–Danforth or coming from University will occupy the upper level. Escalators will be in use for passengers going up between the platforms or to the street, and downward movement will be by fixed stairs.

Experiments are being made with closed circuit television at St. George to enable staff at the east entrance (Bedford Street) to monitor passengers at the west entrance (St. George Street) and control them by a public address system. It is intended to withdraw staff from the west entrance, the passengers gaining entry by unclimbable turnstiles, which will only accept the correct fare in cash or token.

The Bloor–Danforth Line is being built by nine contractors under 14 major contracts. The soil is variable, clay, sand and silt with boulders and over long sections there is ground water. Over the greater part of the 8 miles the alignment avoids the main thoroughfare and runs beneath a secondary road or beneath properties. The cost of acquiring property is expected to be offset by the saving in avoiding the interference with already congested traffic and services beneath the street, and parts of the tunnel are designed with a view to the erection of buildings above them, up to 20 stories high, which should provide a substantial contribution to the cost of the line.

In general the structure is a cut and cover tunnel with the same dimensions as the Yonge Street Line, but over a distance of 2250 ft where the line dips to a depth of 40 ft to pass under the University and Yonge Street Lines, a cast iron tube has been constructed. On this section an interesting comparison of speed and cost was possible, between an existing shield from the University Line work and a rotary digger shield belonging to the contractors, on tunnels with a 17 ft 6 in external diameter. The mechanical shield tunnelled 20 ft per day compared with 9 ft by hand digging.

Over Rosedale Valley, east of Sherbourne, there is an interesting bridge. Seven 48-ft approach spans and a main arch of 206 ft in reinforced concrete form a complete box structure around the track, which is on a curve. The roof has no structural function but is there to reduce the noise nuisance to adjacent residential buildings. This forms an approach to the Don River which is crossed below an existing road bridge which had been designed and built in 1917 for an additional deck by leaving spaces in the piers. It was only necessary to complete a 1484-ft long concrete deck to carry the railway.

The track gauge is 4 ft 10$\frac{7}{8}$ in, following the practice of the local tramways. The rails are 100 lb/yd flat-bottomed throughout, with hemlock sleepers and ballast in the open and on all turnouts, but in the tunnels the arrangement is of the modern type with the rails bolted directly to the concrete invert, with rubber pads $\frac{1}{2}$ in thick and steel base plates, by $\frac{7}{8}$-in steel bolts. This type of track was chosen after examining an experimental section, 20 years old, on the Philadelphia underground. The rails are in 39-ft lengths thermit-welded into continuous lengths between blockjoints or crossing work. Plastic bonded hardwood blockjoint plates are used in the tunnels. An 85 lb/yd check rail is used on curves of less than 2300 ft radius. This is laid on its side in special chairs at 4 ft centres and provides a flangeway of $1\frac{7}{8}$ in, or 2 in for curves of less than 650 ft radius. The single 150-lb/yd current rail is carried by porcelain insulators upon malleable cast iron brackets bolted down to the concrete in tunnels, and carried by every fourth sleeper in the open, where the sleepers are normally 6 in $\times$ 8 in by 8 ft at 2 ft centres, but 9 ft long for the insulators. The conductor rails are thermit-welded up to 1000 ft long with malleable iron expansion joints. The traction current is 600 V d.c. stepped down from the 13 kV a.c. city supply.

The signalling provides for a minimum headway of two minutes by means of three aspect colour light signals with single rail a.c. track circuits and trainstops worked by 110 V a.c. supply. There are three interlocking sections, St. George, Union Street, and St. Andrew-Osgoode, and between Osgoode and Museum there is an automatic block section on which train movements control the signals. The signalling throughout the University Avenue branch is normally controlled from the main interlocking control room at St. George, but can be controlled from Union Station. At St. George Station trains are controlled by an automatic dispatcher using a prepared schedule perforated upon a clock-driven tape.

The determination of the Toronto authorities to keep abreast of developments is particularly evident in their choice of rolling stock. The original 134 steel cars of the Yonge Street Line were built in Britain and based on London Transport practice. They are 57 ft $1\frac{1}{2}$ in long over buffers, 10 ft 4 in wide, and 12 ft 0 in high from rail level, seating 62 passengers and accommodating 168 standing with three pairs of automatic doors on each side. Nearly 10,000 passengers have been carried in one direction in a quarter

The two bogies, at 54 ft centres, each carry two 125 h.p. motors which drive the 30-in diameter wheels through a Cardan shaft and hypoid gears.

For the University Avenue extension, 36 aluminium cars were ordered from Montreal, the first underground stock ever built in Canada. These cars are exceptionally long, being 74 ft $5\frac{5}{8}$ in over coupling faces, 10 ft $3\frac{1}{2}$ in wide and 12 ft high, and will seat 84 passengers with 226 standing. Four sets of electrically operated doors on each side provide openings 3 ft 9 in wide. The tare weight is only 26·6 tons for a pay load of 22 tons of passengers, and a six-car train has the same capacity as an eight-car train of the older stock but weighs 40 per cent less.

The seating is mainly longitudinal but lateral seats are arranged to divide the car into four distinct areas each served by a pair of doors on either side.

The two bogies, at 54 ft centres, each carry two 125 h.p. motors driving 28 in diameter wheels through a single reduction hypoid right angle drive of 7·11:1 or 7·14:1 ratio. Springing is by a combination of pneumatic and steel coil springs with vertical and lateral hydraulic shock absorbers.

The control system incorporates static components in place of interlocks and relays, braking and acceleration being adjusted to the load by air signals from the pneumatic springing which operate transducers – or variable resistors. The braking is normally rheostatic but is supplemented by an electro-pneumatic system. The degree to which the pneumatic brake operates depends upon the current available for rheostatic braking. Thus the pneumatic system smoothly takes over the duty as the rheostatic brake fades with reducing speed and comes into full operation in case of a failure of the rheostatic system or of the traction current.

It is notable that a failure of rheostatic braking on one car brings in the pneumatic brake on that car only. The pneumatic brake operates by one complete unit of non-metallic shoe, automatic slack adjuster and brake cylinder bolted directly to the cast steel bogie frame. One such unit is provided for each wheel. The air pressure in the brake cylinder is controlled by three factors, the rheostatic braking current, the load on the pneumatic springs, and the position of the drivers control.

Every car has a complete set of traction and braking control gear and they are run in two-car units built up into six-car sets. One car of each unit carries the motor alternator set, rectifiers and batteries for low-voltage d.c. supply and the other car carries the motor-driven compressor unit.

These cars will not couple to the original Yonge Street rolling stock, but for inter-running of old and new trains, their normal acceleration rate of 2·5 m.p.h. per second can be reduced to 1·9 m.p.h. per second by a key-operated switch.

A very complete communication system is provided between

the train and the controller. This is by telephone wires coupled to the contact rails at ¼-mile intervals and operating on an amplitude modulated frequency of 72 kc/s. There is also a public address system from the controller to all trains and from the driver to the passengers on his train, as well as a two-way system between driver and guard.

The exterior is of unpainted aluminium, finished by a stainless steel brush and aluminium extrusions have been used extensively, for the top and bottom rails, door posts and corner posts, louvre frames and trimmings, both inside and outside. Even the side frame and main longitudinal members are of aluminium. The use of steel is virtually confined to the high tensile low alloy ends of under-frames, which are welded to carry cast steel centre bearings and coupling anchors, and the lateral supports beneath the floor and equipment frames.

In the interior there is a minimum of paint. The ceiling and wainscot are in coloured laminated plastic fixed with snap-on aluminium mouldings, and the window surrounds are of bright coloured thermoplastic, vacuum formed. The predominant colours are light blue, yellow and pale grey. The windows are fixed in order to keep out dirt and noise and to conserve the heat of the interior. Ventilation is by five pressure fans per car, each of 3000 ft³/min capacity. Waste heat from the rheostatic braking warms air which is passed through louvres in the aluminium bases of the seats, and this can be supplemented by 24 kW of auxiliary heating. Lighting is by two continuous rows of cool white fluorescent tubes and an emergency light is fitted over each door.

The rolling stock is now maintained at Davisville, which is full to capacity with the existing fleet of cars. With the opening of the first section of the Bloor–Danforth Subway another 100 cars will be required, and to work the complete system now under construction a total of 328 cars will be required. Therefore the first section of the Bloor–Danforth Subway will include a new depot to the south of the line, between the stations at Donlands and Greenwood. This will be a single-ended depot with connection to both main lines. It will cover more than 38 acres with stabling on fans to the west, a large maintenance shop near the entrance on the east, with washing and inspectors' sheds also on the same side.

Vienna

Vienna was a pioneer city in the development of trams and still shows no sign of abandoning tramways, as most other capital cities are doing. Instead the city is engaged upon a very extensive programme of traffic engineering, in the course of which tramways are being put underground and becoming more akin to underground railways.

Until a century ago Vienna was heavily fortified and the city plan is still characterized by the ring roads which follow the concentric lines of the old fortifications and trenches. In 1865, after these had been dismantled, the first horse trams were in operation. In 1883 there were steam trams. Experiments with electrification started in 1894 and the first electric tram ran in 1897. By that date there were already 112 km (70 miles) of tramway worked by two private companies until they were taken over by the municipality on July 1, 1903, and the last horse-drawn tram ran in June 1903.

The Vienna Municipal Transport Undertaking (Wiener Stadtwerke Verkehrsbetriebe) now operates 235 miles of tramway or 152 route miles on 55 routes, and 127 miles of bus routes as well as the Municipal Railway or Stadtbahn. The heart of the city with its narrow streets can only be served by motor buses, while the tram network is based upon two circular streets, the Ringstrasse or inner circle and the Gurtel or outer circle, on the site of the old fortifications, and upon radial lines leading outwards from these. The Stadtbahn does not run through the centre of the city, but follows the Gurtel (outer ring road), the River Wien and the Danube canal. It was opened with steam power in 1898 to connect the main line stations of the National Railways and was electrified in 1924.

By 1945 Vienna had lost 60 per cent of her trams and urban rolling stock in the war and the permanent way and fixed installations had been largely destroyed, while private transport was virtually non-existent. Reconstruction had to wait until Austrian industry could accept orders for rolling stock, and was not completed until 1963.

The Stadtbahn consists of 26½ route km (16½ miles) of double track of which 6½ km (4 miles) is in tunnel. In general the tunnels are of cut and cover type with vertical walls 10 m (33 ft) apart and an arched roof nearly 6 m (19 ft 6 in) high, but in places they are of circular cross section having a diameter of 9 m (29 ft 6 in).

The trains are usually of six or seven cars, though as many as nine cars are sometimes coupled together. There are 25 stations with low side platforms and exceptionally good transfer facilities with the tram routes overhead.

The 130 motors and 200 trailers are of a two-axled tramway type with seats for 20 passengers and room for about 50 standing. The overall length is 10·7 m (35 ft 1 in) and the width is 2·22 m (7 ft 3½ in) with two pairs of doors in each side. The line is sharply curved with a minimum radius of 50 m (164 ft) and a ruling gradient of 1 in 33, both in accordance with tramway rather than railway standards. The single overhead pantographs on the cars collect 750 V d.c. current which has been stepped down from the 5-kV supply of the Vienna Electricity Works at four substations.

The track gauge is 1·44 m (4 ft 8¾ in) and the rails are 43 and 77 kg/m (85 and 145 lb/yd). In places the tracks are laid on a base of rubber and cork while the roofs of the tunnels are also lined to reduce noise. Railway type automatic block signalling with two aspect colour lights and track circuiting are installed.

The Stadtbahn is really only an important part of the tramway system upon which a fleet of 1146 driven and 1272 trailing trams are operated. This tramway system is underground over 1900 m (1·18 miles) near Alserstrasse and a subway of 1870 m is planned along the Gurtel from Sudtirolerplatz. At Sudtirolerplatz the trams are already in a tunnel where the Gurtel, trams and Schnellbahn (suburban railway) pass under the radial thoroughfare and tram routes. Here there is a joint station with shop windows and showcases, wide low level platforms with six escalators and 10 stairways between the two levels. At Schottentor also a remarkable transfer station was opened in September 1961. Here the Ringstrasse passes beneath two parallel radial streets in which six tram lines carrying very heavy traffic have their termini. Two reversing loops have been provided, one above the other, and the platforms are connected by six pairs of stairways and five escalators.

This constant process of taking tramways underground, coupling the vehicles together and providing full station facilities makes Vienna a fine field for argument over the distinction between an underground railway and a tramway.